Born This Way

Words & Music by Stefani Germanotta, Jeppe Laursen,
Fernando Garibay & Paul Blair

WISE PUBLICATIONS
PART OF THE MUSIC SALES GROUP
LONDON / NEW YORK / PARIS / SYDNEY / COPENHAGEN / BERLIN / MADRID / HONG KONG / TOKYO

Published by

WISE PUBLICATIONS
14-15 Berners Street, London W1T 3LJ, UK

Exclusive Distributors:

MUSIC SALES LIMITED
Distribution Centre, Newmarket Road,
Bury St Edmunds, Suffolk IP33 3YB, UK

MUSIC SALES PTY LIMITED
20 Resolution Drive,
Caringbah, NSW 2229, Australia

Order No. AM1003409
ISBN 978-1-78038-098-8

Edited by Jenni Wheeler.
Cover designed by Lizzie Barrand.

Printed in the EU

www.musicsales.com

G5
F5
C5
3fr
1. My ma-ma told me when I was young "We're all born su-per-stars."
She rolled my hair, put my lip-stick on in the glass of her bou-doir.
"There's noth-ing wrong with lov-ing who you are" she said,
A diff-'rent lov-er is not a sin. Be-lieve

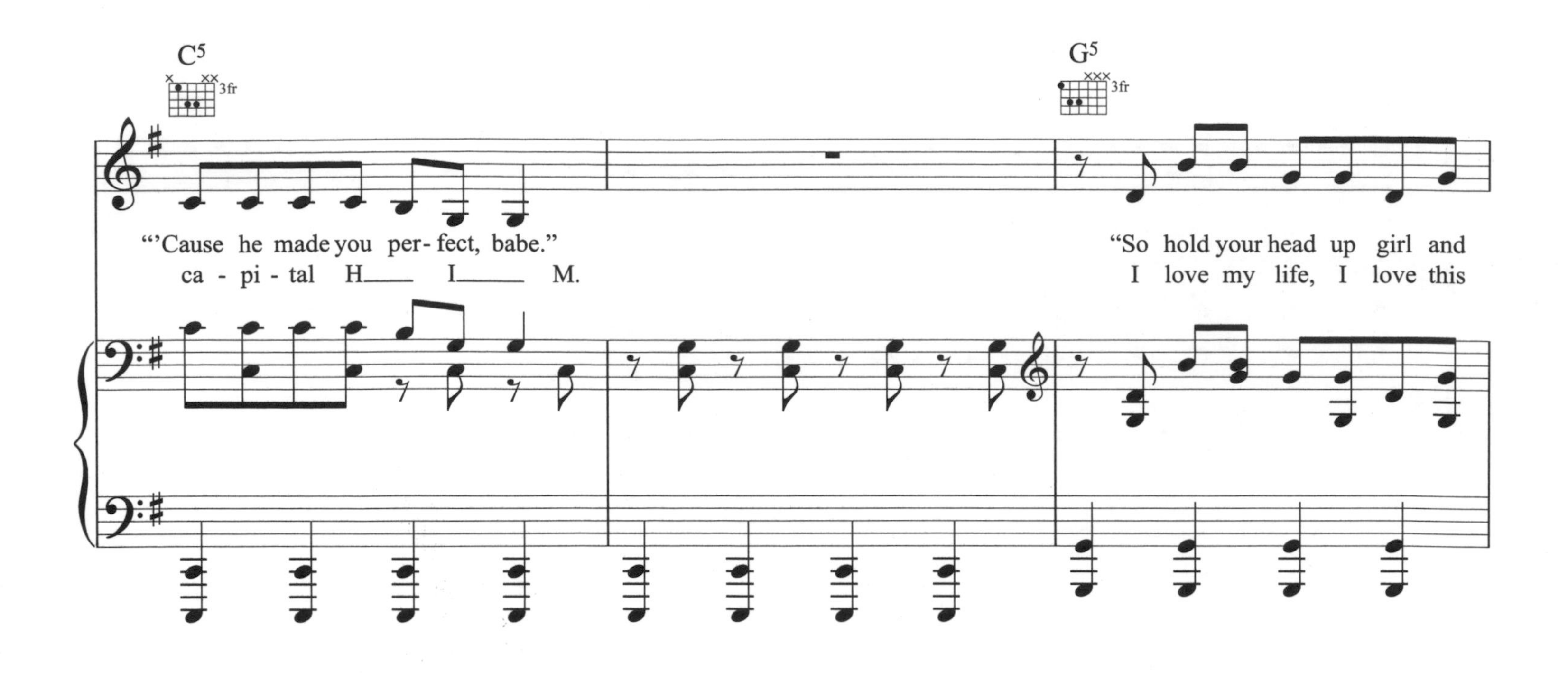
C5
3fr
G5
3fr
"'Cause he made you per-fect, babe."
"So hold your head up girl and
ca - pi - tal H I M.
I love my life, I love this

F5
C5
3fr
G5
3fr
you'll go far.
Lis - ten to me when I say:"
I'm beau - ti -
re - cord and
mi a - mo - re vo - le fe, yah.

F5
C5
3fr
-ful in my way 'cause God makes no mis - takes I'm on the right track, ba - by, I was

G5
3fr
F5
born this way. Don't hide your - self in re - gret. Just love your - self and you're set. I'm on the
C5
3fr
G5
3fr
right track, ba - by, I was born this way, born this way. Ooh, there ain't no oth - er way.
F5
C5
3fr
G5
3fr
C/G
Ba - by, I was born this way. Ba - by, I was born this_ way, born this way.
G5
3fr
F5
C5
3fr
To Coda
Ooh, there ain't no oth - er way. Ba - by, I was born this way. Right track, ba - by, I was

G5
3fr
N.C.
born this way. Don't be a drag, just be a queen. Don't be a drag, just be a queen. Don't
be a drag, just be a queen. (Don't be, don't be, don't be...)
G5
F5
C5
2. Give your-self pru-dence and love your friends. Sub-way kid, re-joice your truth.
G5
F5
In the re-li-gion of the in-se-cure I must

C5
3fr
D.S. al Coda
G5
3fr
be my- self, re spect my youth.
born_ this way._
3
Dm
(Way. Don't be, don't, don't be... way...) Don't be a drag,_ just be a queen._Wheth-
-er you're broke_ or ev-er-green._You're black, white, beige, cho-la des-cent,_you're Le-ba-nese,_you're o - ri-ent._Wheth-
G5
3fr
-er life's dis - a - bi - li - ties_ left you out-cast, bul-lied, or teased,_ re - joice and love your-self to-day_'cause

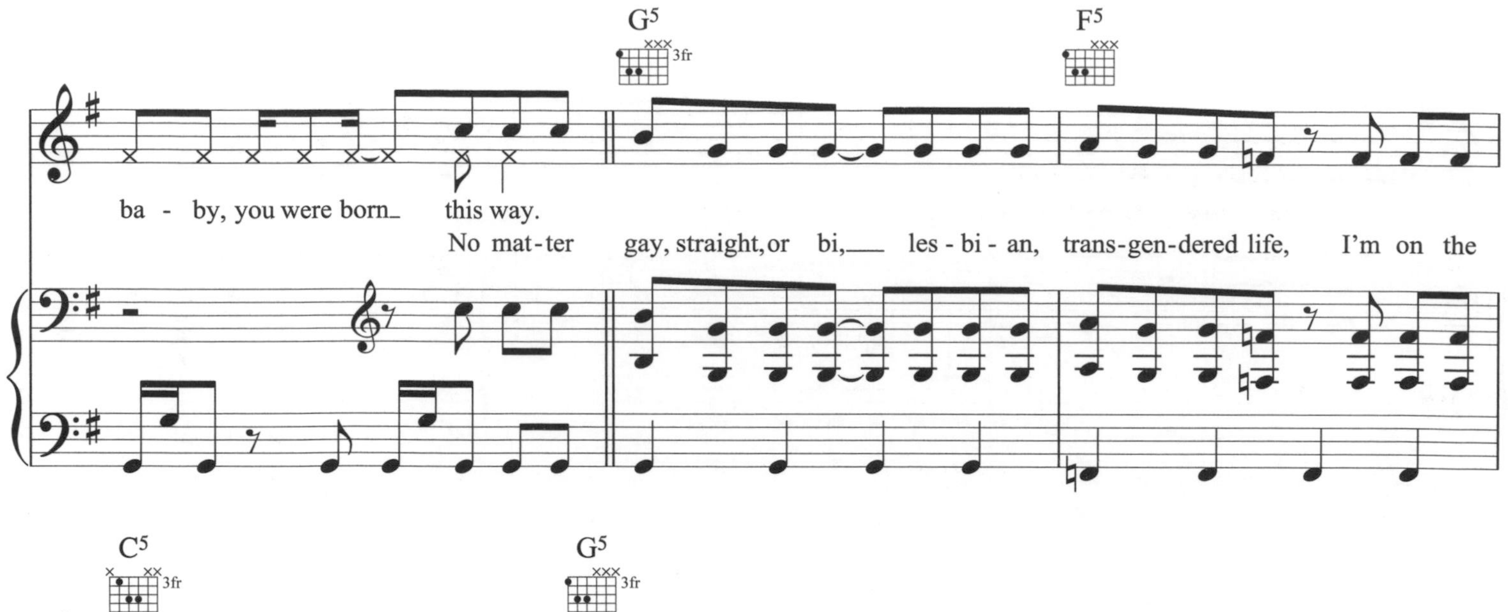
G5
3fr
F5
ba - by, you were born this way.
No mat - ter gay, straight, or bi, les - bi - an, trans - gen - dered life, I'm on the

C5
3fr
G5
3fr
right track, ba - by, I was born to sur - vive. No mat - ter black, white or beige, cho - la or

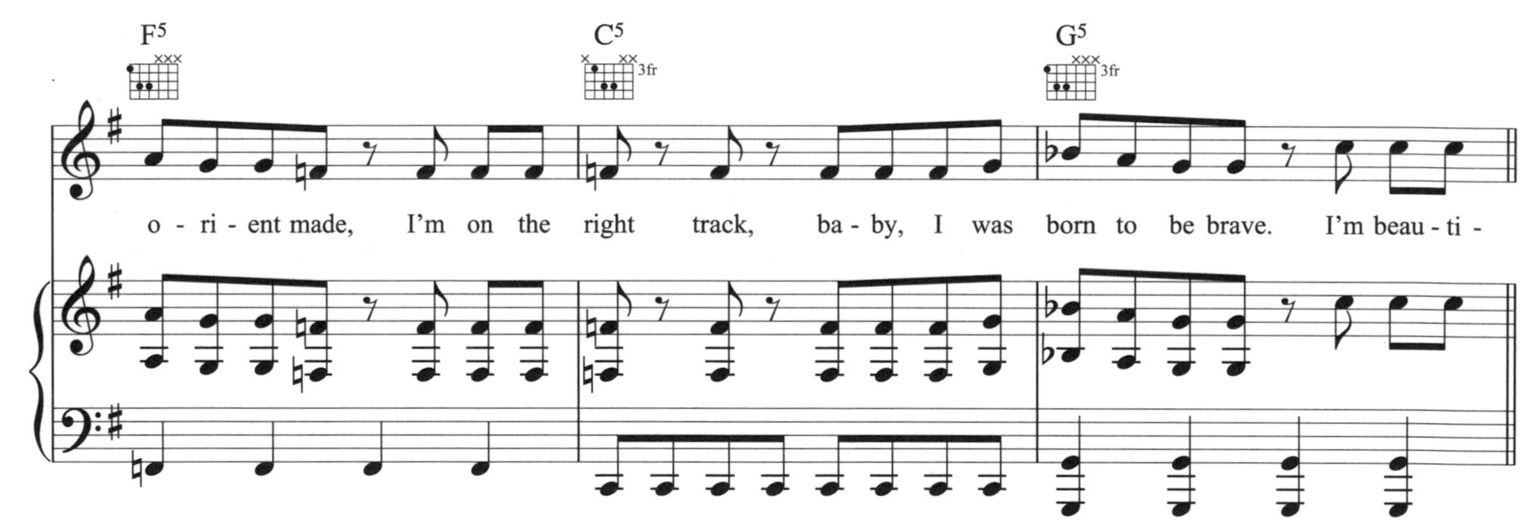
F5
C5
3fr
G5
3fr
o - ri - ent made, I'm on the right track, ba - by, I was born to be brave. I'm beau - ti -

F5
C5
3fr
- ful in my way 'cause God makes no mis - takes I'm on the right track, ba - by, I was

G5
3fr
F5
born this way. Don't hide your - self in re - gret. Just love your - self and you're set. I'm on the
C5
3fr
G5
3fr
right track, ba - by, I was born this way, yeah! Ooh, there ain't no oth - er way.
F5
C5
3fr
G5
3fr
C7/G
Ba - by, I was born this way. Ba - by, I was born this, way, born this way.
F5
C5
3fr
Ooh, there ain't no oth - er way. Ba - by, I was born this way. Right track, ba - by, I was

G5
3fr
G5
3fr
F5
born this way. I was born this way, hey! I was born this way, hey! I'm on the
C5
3fr
G5
3fr
N.C.
right track, ba - by, I was born this way, hey! I was born this way hey! I was
born this way hey! I'm on the right track ba - by I was born this way hey!

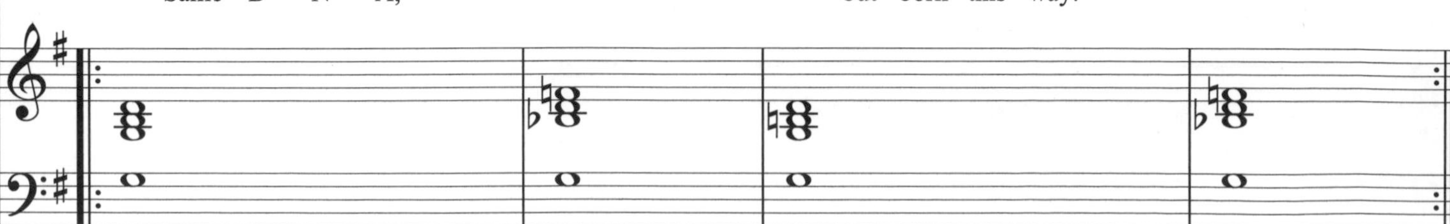
G
Gm7
3fr
G
Gm7
3fr
Same D N A, but born this way.

Eyes Wide Shut

Words & Music by Lars Jensen, Oritsé Williams, Marvin Humes,
Jonathan Gill, Aston Merrygold & Tim McEwan

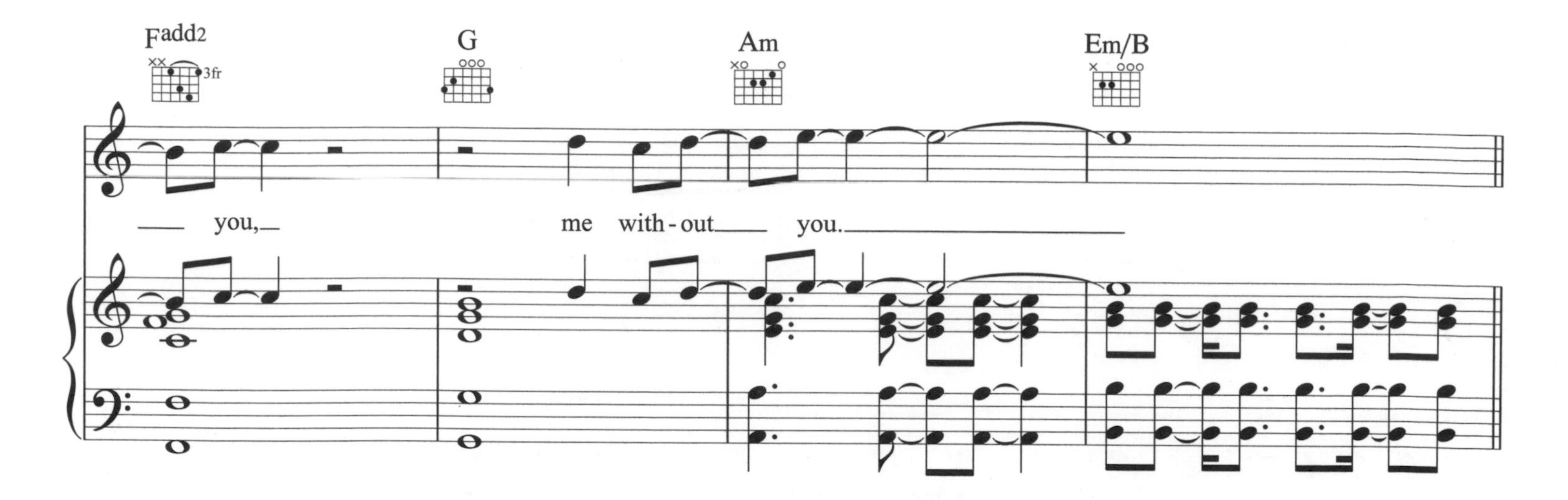
Fadd2
3fr
G
Am
Em/B
you,
me with-out you.

F
G
Am
N.C.
Em
F
N.C.
(Yeah,
F
G
Am
Em
F
yeah, yeah.)
Don't tell me I'm dream-
G
Am
Em
F
-in' 'cause if I've been dream-in',
I, I, I, I don't ev-er want to wake

G
Am
up. So in love with this feel - in' to-night I'll be sleep - in',
Em
F
sleep - in' with my eyes wide shut. 'Cause I don't want to wake up,
G
Am
Em
F
wake up, wake up. I don't want to wake up, wake up, wake up.
G
Am
So in love with this feel - in' to-night I'll be sleep - in',

Em
F
F
sleep-in' with my eyes wide shut.
2. Out of sight, they say,
G
Am
C
out of mind;
but your im-age will re-main till the end of time.

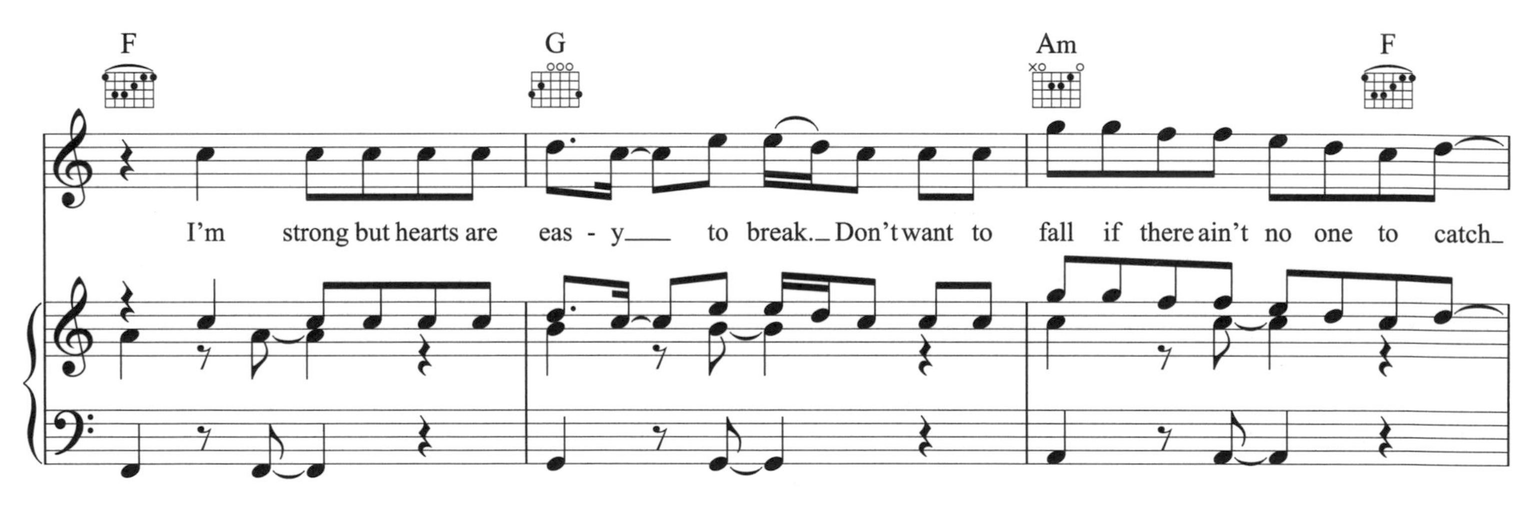
F
G
Am
F
I'm strong but hearts are eas-y to break. Don't want to fall if there ain't no one to catch

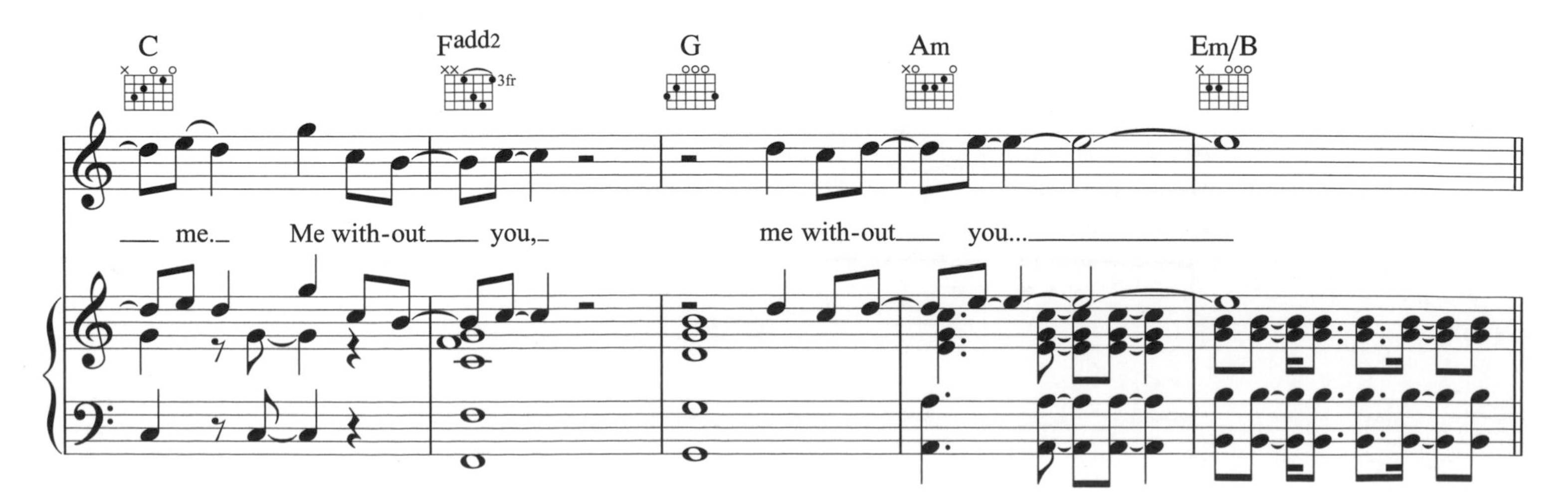
C
Fadd2
3fr
G
Am
Em/B
me. Me with-out you, me with-out you...

F
G
Am
Em
F
Oh,___
I don't ev - er want to wake
F
G
Am
up. Don't tell me I'm dream - in' 'cause if I've been dream - in',___ I, I, I,
Em
F
G
Am
I don't ev - er want to wake up. So in love with this feel - in' to-night I'll be sleep-
Em
F
- in',___ sleep-in' with my eyes___ wide shut. 'Cause I don't want to wake up,___

G
Am
Em
F
wake up,
wake up.
I don't want to wake up,
wake up,
wake up.
G
Am
So in love with this feel - in'
to-night I'll be sleep - in',
Em
F
To Coda
F
sleep-in' with my eyes wide
shut.
Ev-'ry - bod-y ev-'ry-where, throw your
G
Am
C
hands in the air. Say "yeah,"
say "yeah, yeah,
yeah." Go

F
G
Am
put your hands high if you ain't sleep-in' to - night. Say "yeah, yeah,
C
F
G
Am
yeah, yeah, yeah." Your love,
oh...
oh...
oh...

Em
F
G
Am

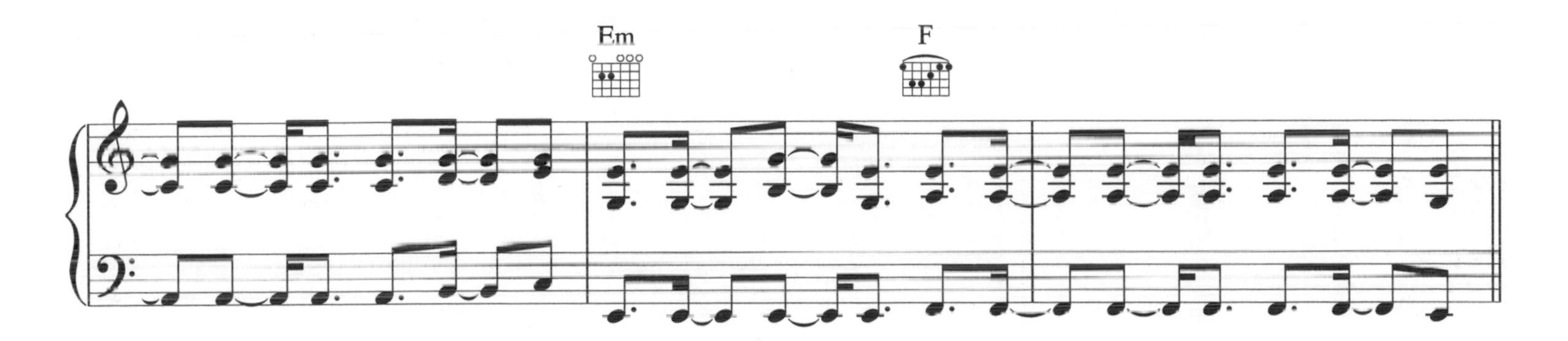
Em
F

G
Am
To - night I'll be sleep -
Em
F
D.S. al Coda
- in'...
Don't tell me I'm dream -
Coda
F
G
Am
- bod - y ev - 'ry - where, throw your hands in the air. Say
Em
F
G
Am
"yeah," say "yeah, yeah, yeah." Go put your hands high if you ain't

Em
F
sleep- in' to - night Say "yeah, yeah, yeah, yeah, yeah."
G
Am
Em
F
Sleep- in' with my eyes wide
shut, eyes wide shut, eyes wide
G
Am
Em
F
shut.

Don't Hold Your Breath

Words & Music by Billy Steinberg, Joshua Berman & Tobias Gad

D♭
4fr
Fm
E♭
6fr
N.C.
think I'm com - in' back, don't hold your breath.
8vb till *
1. I was un - der your spell for such a long time, could-n't break the chains.
2. I was wor - ried a - bout you, but you nev - er cared a - bout me none.
You played with my heart, tore me a - part with all your lies and games.
You took my mon - ey and I know that you, you could kill some - one.
1° only
It took all the strength I had but I crawled up on my feet a - gain.

D♭
4fr
Fm
E♭
6fr
Now you're try - in' to lure me back, but no, those days have gone my friend.
I loved you so much that I thought some - day that you could change.
I gave you ev - 'ry - thing but noth - ing was ev - er e - nough.
N.C.
But all you brought me was a heart full of pain.
You were al - ways jea - lous o - ver such cra - zy stuff.
* You
can't touch me now, there's no feel - in' left. If you think I'm com - in' back, don't

Fm
E♭
D♭
Fm
E♭
6fr
4fr
hold your breath.
What you did to me, boy, I can't forget. If you
D♭
Fm
E♭
1.
D♭maj9
think I'm com - in' back, don't hold your breath.
Don't
Fm
E♭
D♭maj9
Fm
E♭
hold your breath.
2.
E♭
B♭m7
D♭
Fm
Don't hold your breath.
Move on.

E♭
6fr
B♭m
D♭
4fr
Don't look back.
8vb till *
I jumped off the train run-nin' off
Fm
E♭
6fr
B♭m
3
the tracks. Your day's gone, face the facts. A bad
D♭
4fr
Fm
D♭maj9
mo-vie ends and the screen fades to black. What you did to me, boy, I
Fm
E♭
6fr
D♭maj9
D♭
4fr
can't for-get. If you think I'm com-in' back...
echo
* You

D♭
4fr
Fm
E♭
6fr
D♭
4fr
can't touch me now, there's no feel - in' left. If you think I'm com- in' back,_ don't
Fm
E♭
6fr
D♭
4fr
Fm
E♭
6fr
hold your breath.___ What you did to me, boy, I can't for- get. If you
1.
2.
D♭
4fr
Fm
E♭
6fr
Fm
E♭
6fr
D♭maj9
think I'm com- in' back,_ don't hold your breath._ You hold your breath.___
Fm
E♭
6fr
D♭add9
Fm
E♭
6fr
D♭
4fr
Ooh.___

Gold Forever

Words & Music by Wayne Hector, Steve Mac & Kelly Claude

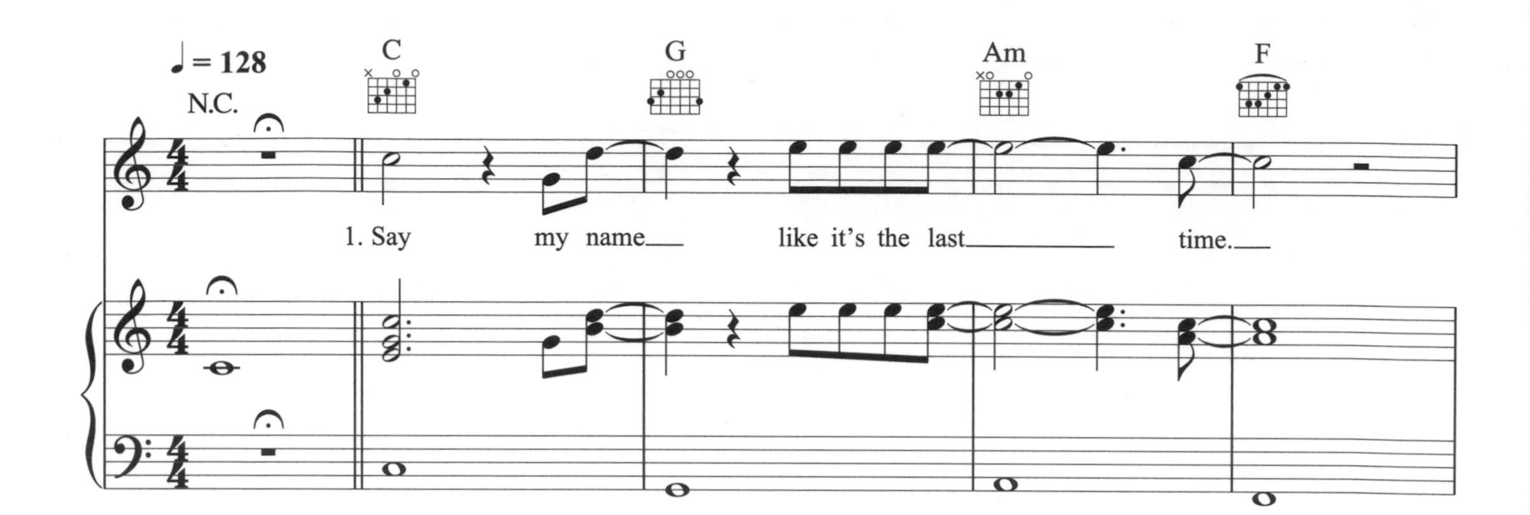

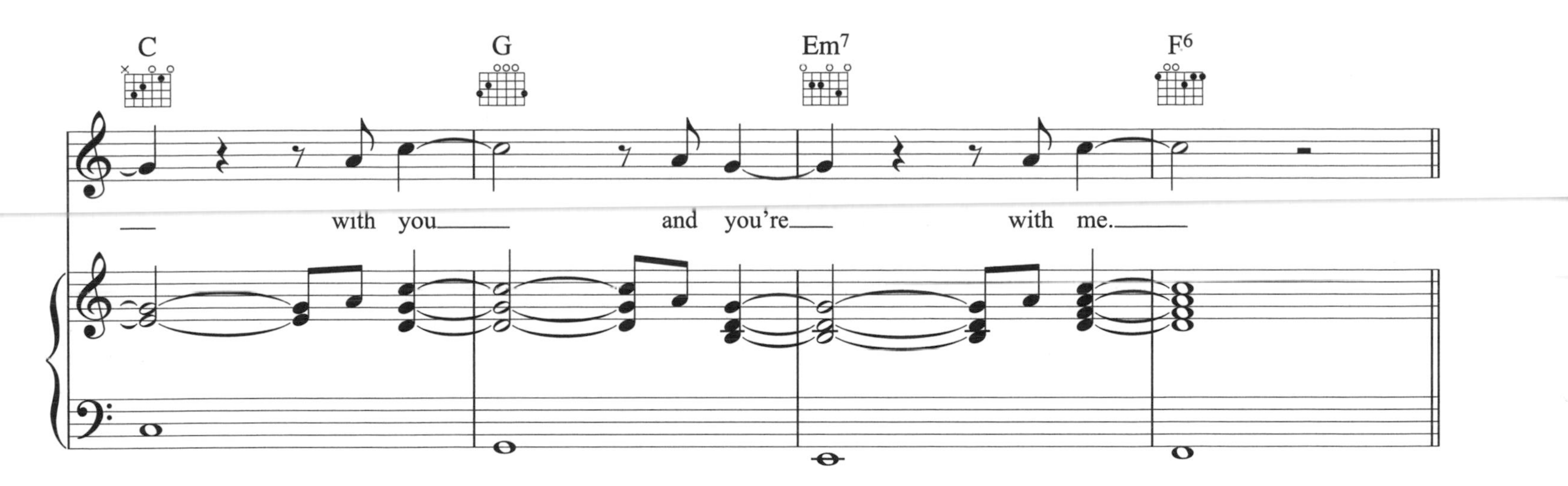
C
G
Em7
F6
with you and you're with me.

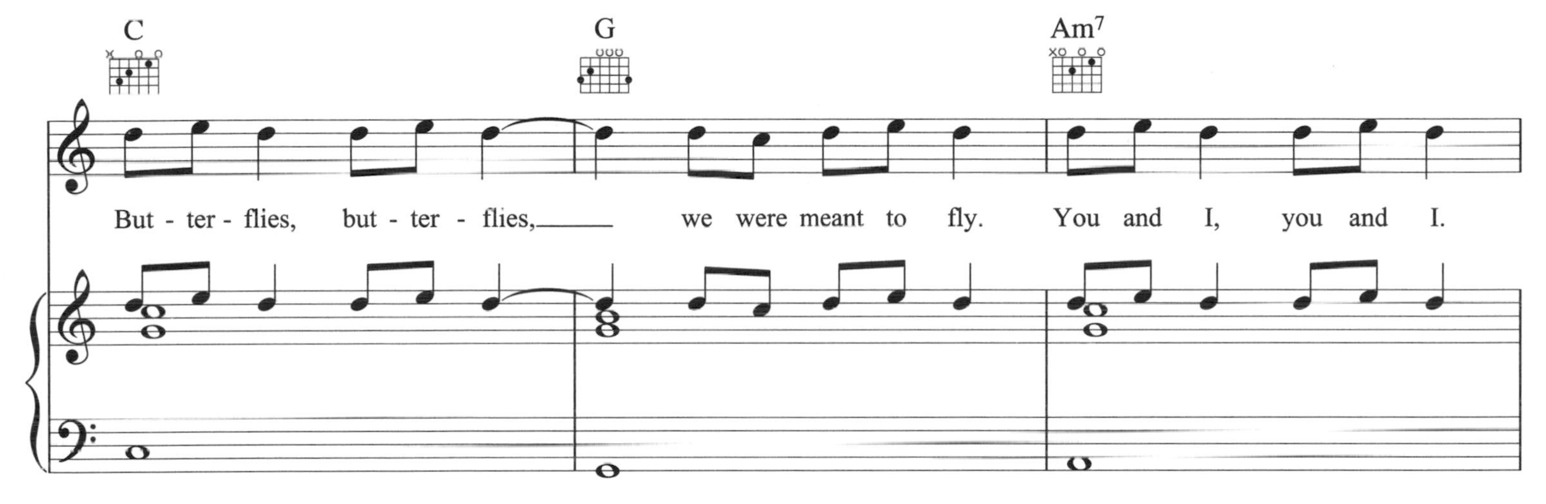
C
G
Am7
But - ter - flies, but - ter - flies, we were meant to fly. You and I, you and I.

F
C
G
Col - ours in the sky. We could rule the world some day, some - how, but we'll

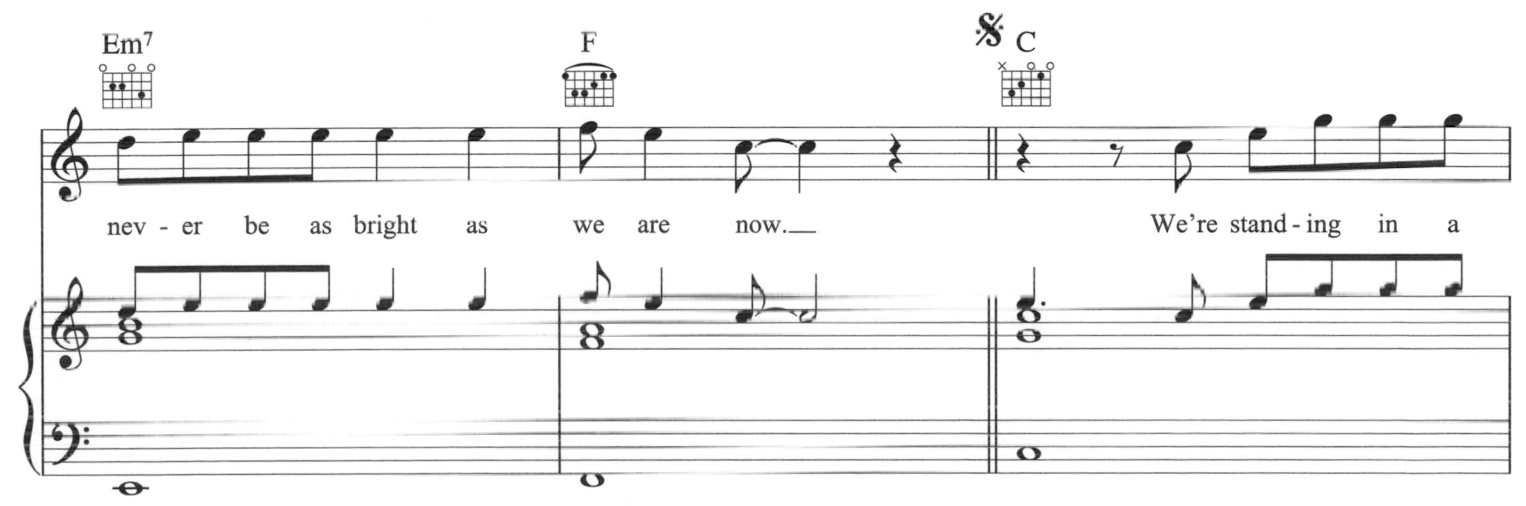
Em7
F
C
nev - er be as bright as we are now. We're stand - ing in a

G
Am7
F
C
light that won't fade. To-mor-row's com-ing but this won't change, 'cause some-days

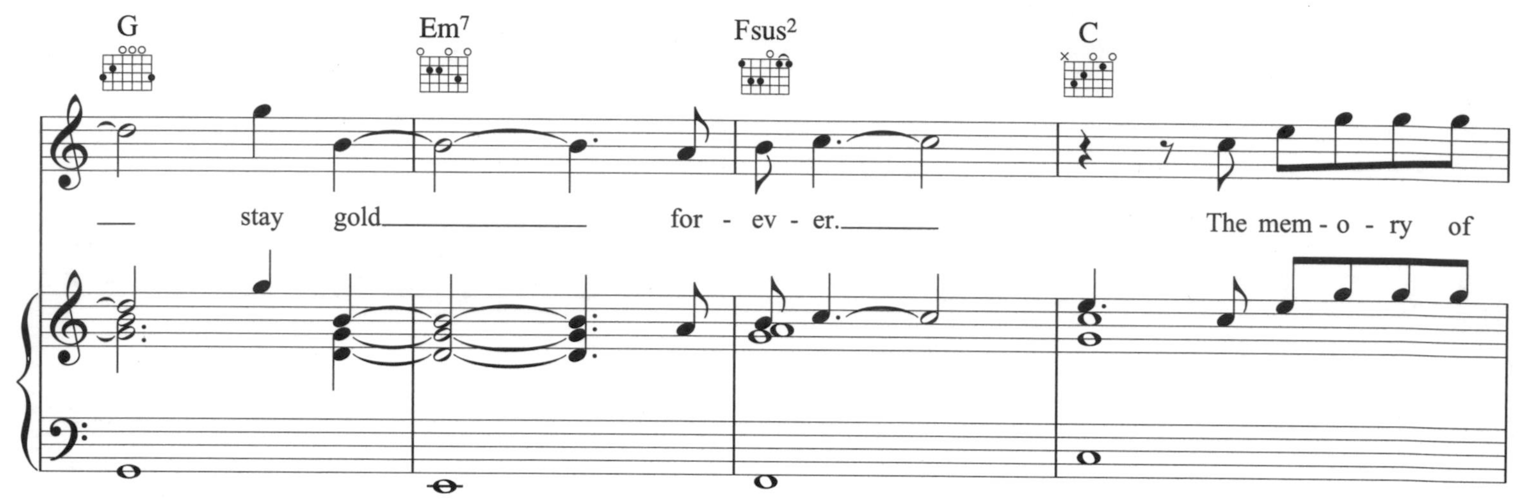
G
Em7
Fsus2
C
stay gold for - ev - er. The mem - o - ry of

G
Am
F
C
be - ing here with you is what I'm gon - na take my life through. 'Cause some days

G
Em7
To Coda N.C.
F
stay gold for - ev - er.

C
G
Am
F

C
G
Em7
F

C
G
Am
2. Prom - ise me you'll stay the way you are.

F
C
G
Keep the fire a - live and stay young

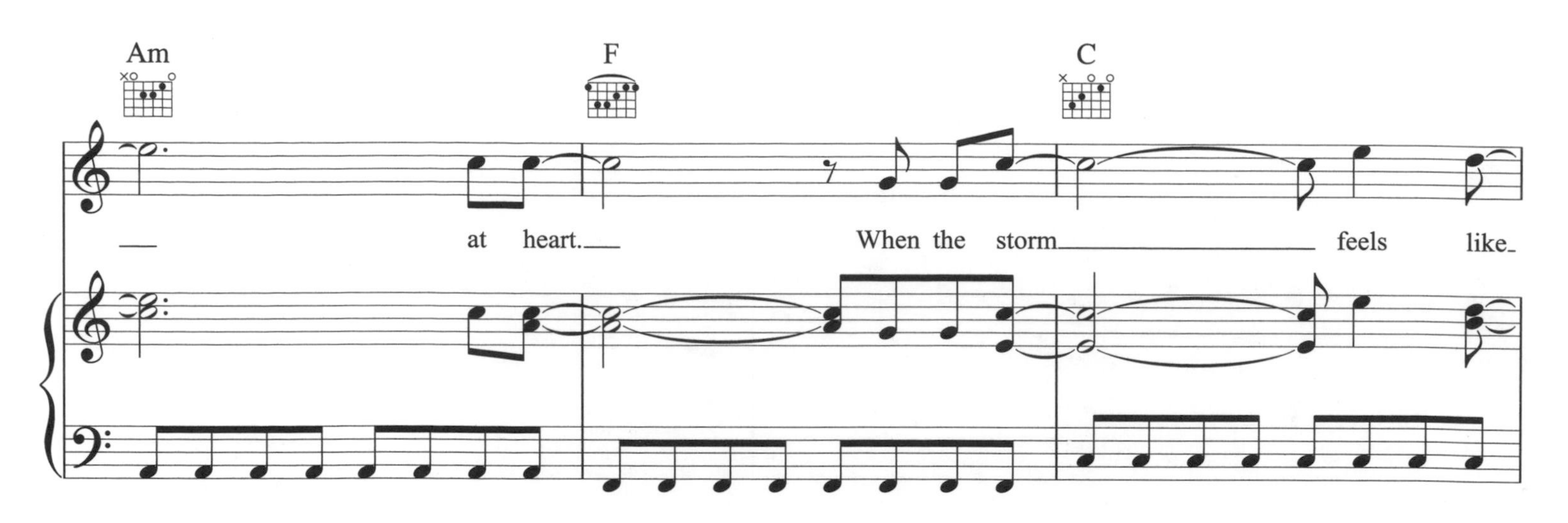
Am
F
C
at heart.
When the storm
feels like

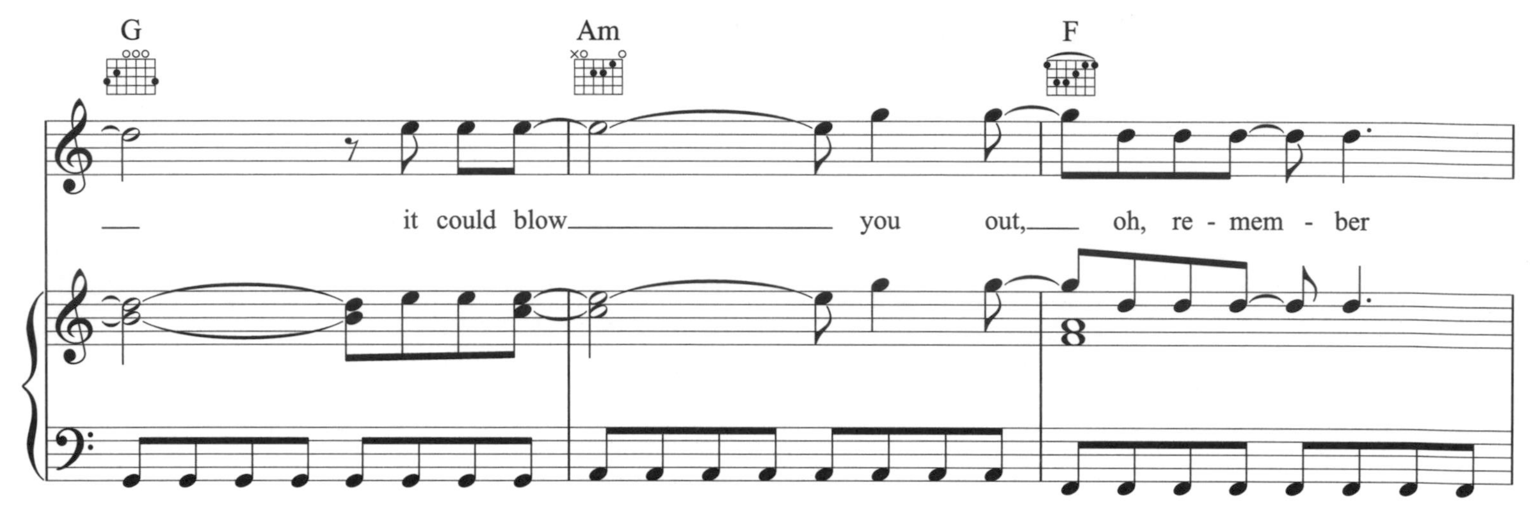
G
Am
F
it could blow
you
out,
oh, re - mem - ber

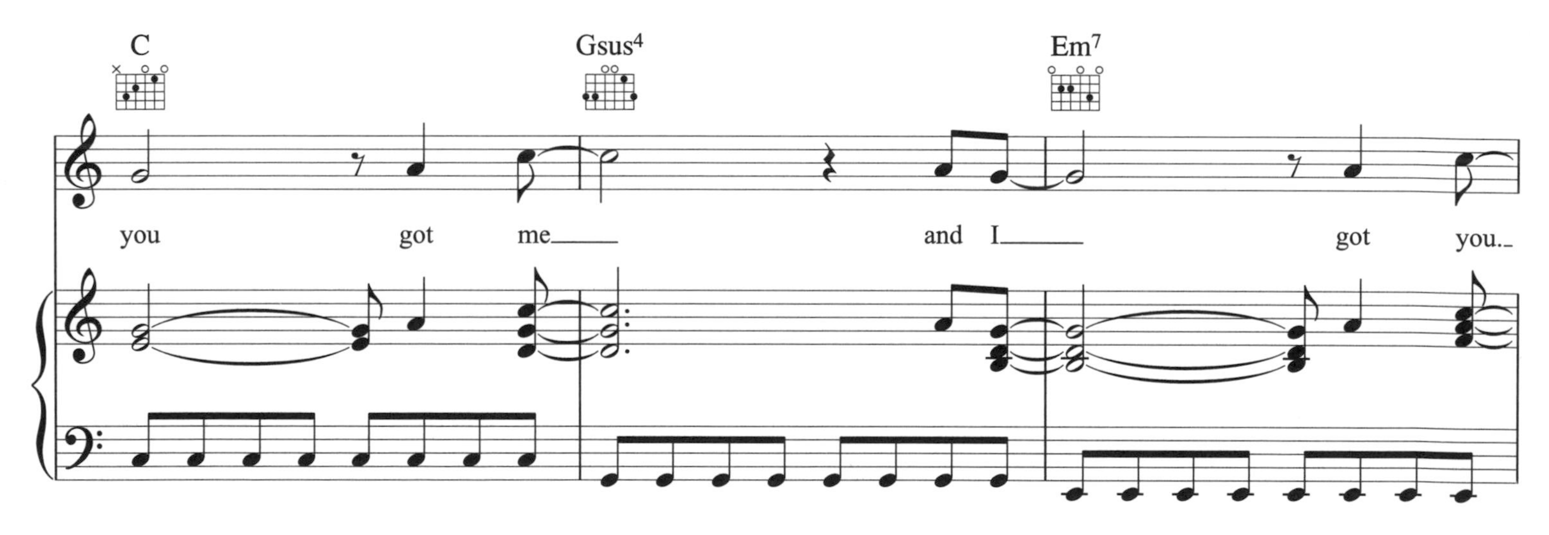
C
Gsus4
Em7
you
got
me
and I
got
you.

F
C
G
'Cause we
are
but - ter - flies,
but - ter - flies,
we were meant to
fly.

Am7
F
C
You and I, you and I. Colours in the sky. When the in-no-cence is

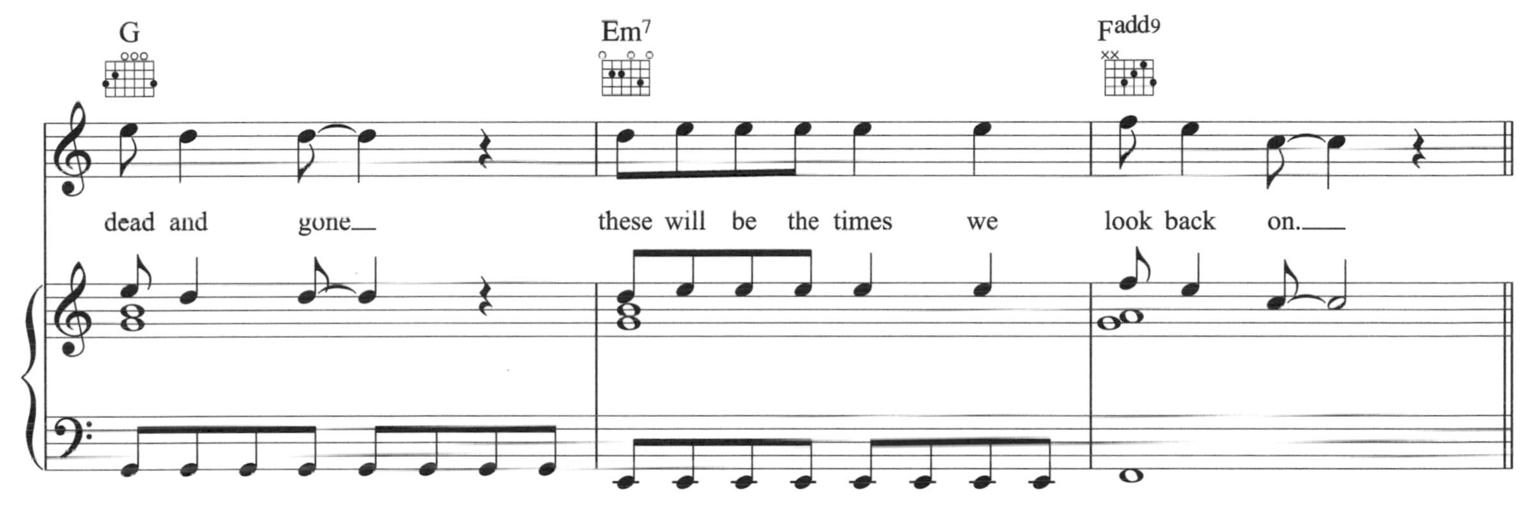
G
Em7
Fadd9
dead and gone these will be the times we look back on.

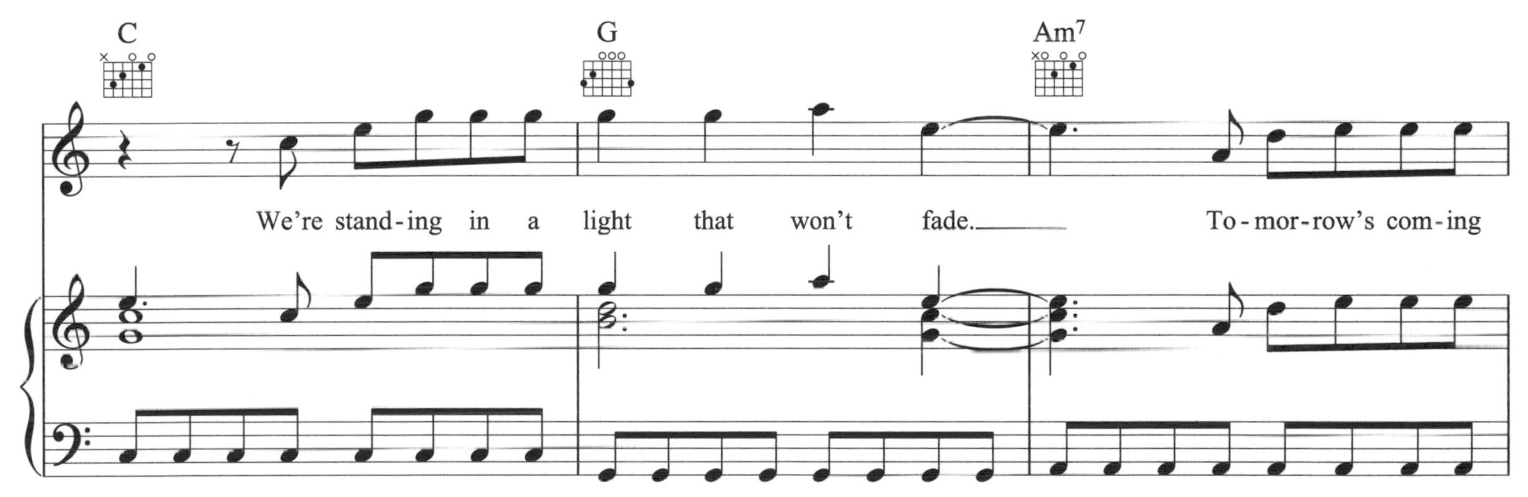
C
G
Am7
We're stand-ing in a light that won't fade. To-mor-row's com-ing

F
C
G
but this won't change, 'cause some - days stay gold

Em7
Fsus2
C
for - ev - er.
The mem - o - ry of

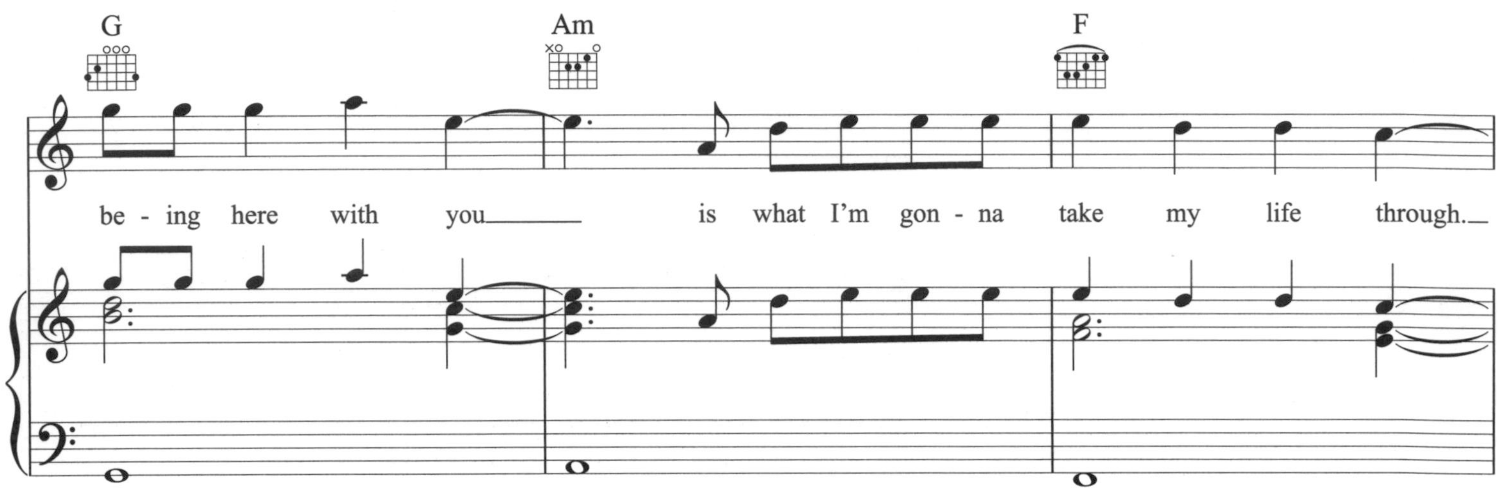

G
Am
F
be - ing here with you
is what I'm gon - na take my life through.

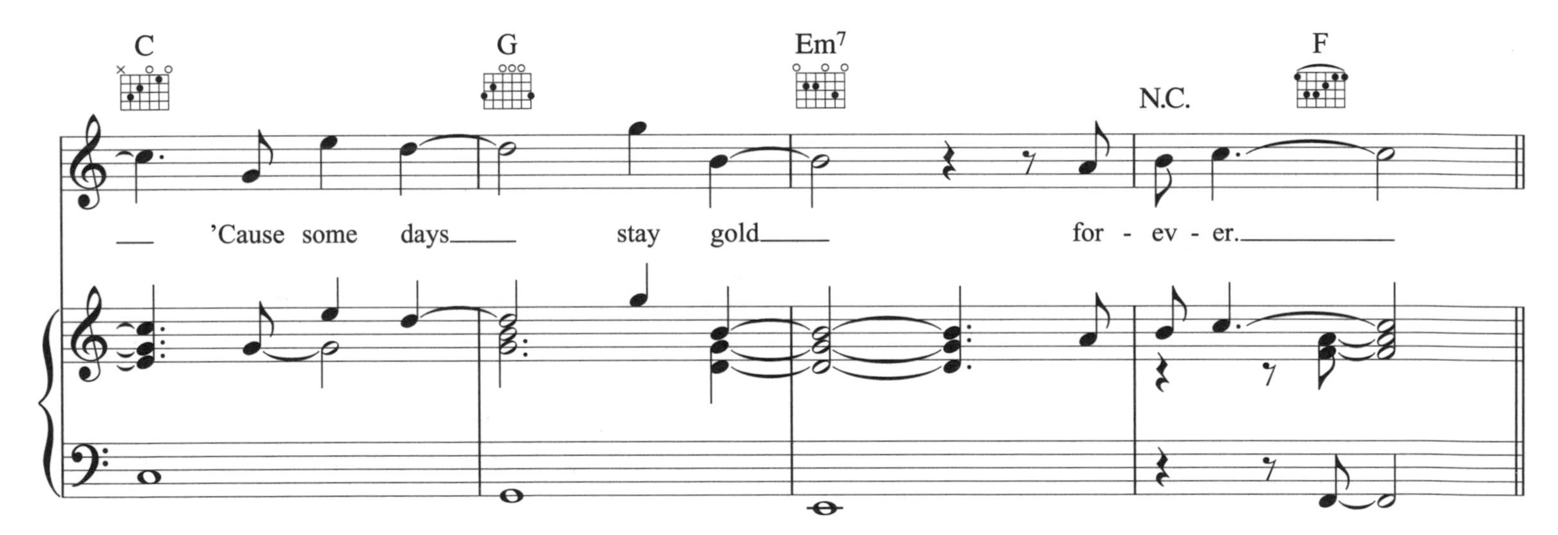

C
G
Em7
N.C.
F
'Cause some days stay gold for - ev - er.

C
G
Am
F
I won't, I won't let your mem - o - ry go 'cause your col - ours, they burn so bright.

C
G
Em
Who knows, who knows what to - mor-row will hold but I know that we'll be al -
Fmaj7
C
G
- right. 'Cause we're but - ter- flies, but - ter - flies, we were meant to fly.
Am7
F
C
G
You and I, you and I. Col-ours in the sky. We could rule the world some day, some - how, but we'll
Em7
Fadd9
D.S. al Coda
Coda
F
nev - er be as bright as we are now.
- ev - er.

Grenade

Words & Music by Phillip Lawrence, Peter Hernandez, Christopher Brown,
Ari Levine, Claude Kelly & Andrew Wyatt

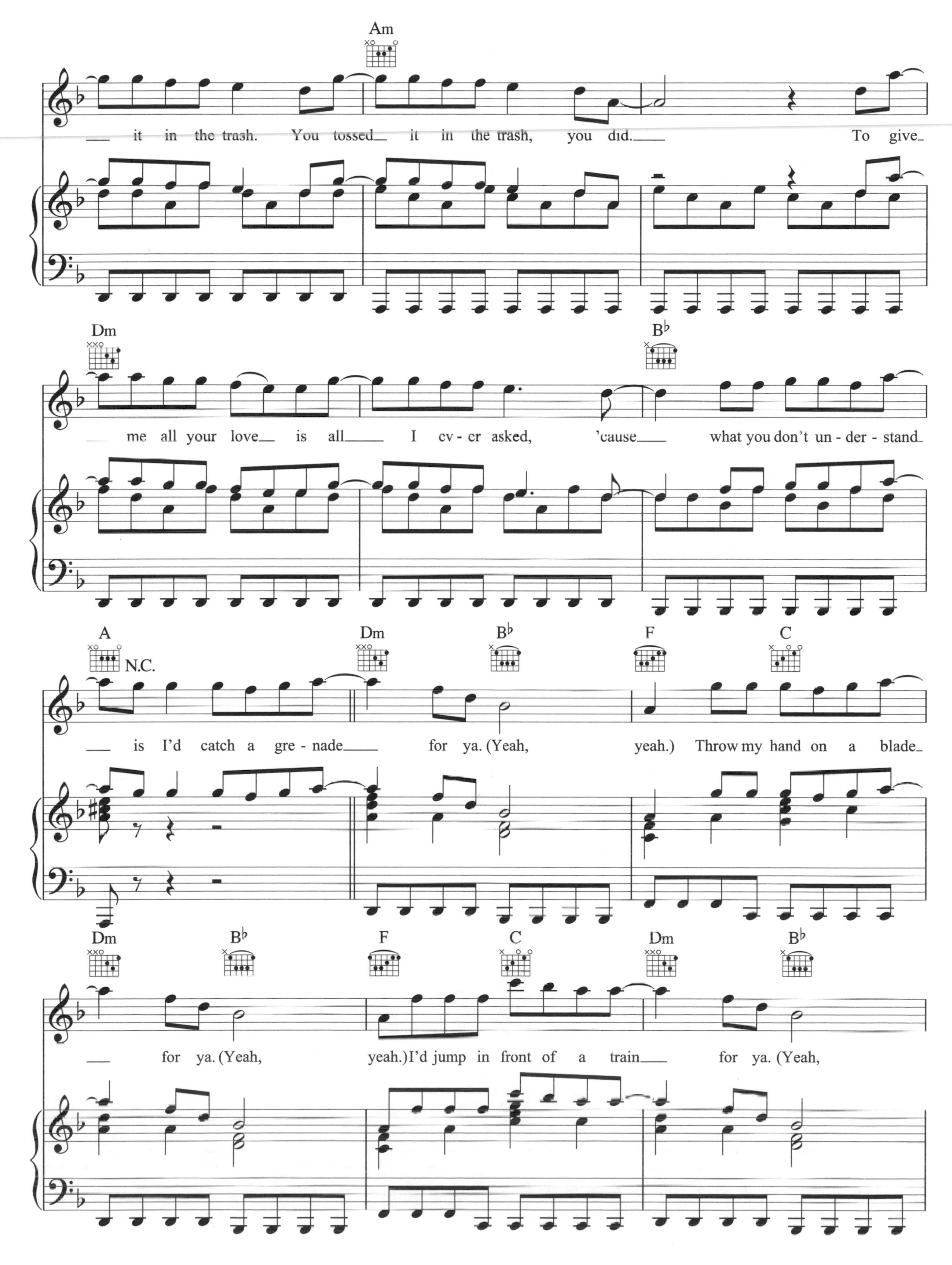
Am
it in the trash. You tossed it in the trash, you did. To give
Dm
B♭
me all your love is all I ev - er asked, 'cause what you don't un - der - stand
A
N.C.
Dm
B♭
F
C
is I'd catch a gre - nade for ya. (Yeah, yeah.) Throw my hand on a blade
Dm
B♭
F
C
Dm
B♭
for ya. (Yeah, yeah.) I'd jump in front of a train for ya. (Yeah,

F C Dm B♭ F C
yeah.) You know I'd do an - y - thing for ya. (Yeah, yeah.) Oh, oh. I would
B♭ C F A
go through all this pain, take a bul - let straight through my brain.
Dm C B♭ A N.C.
Yes, I would die for you ba - by, but you won't do the same.
1.
Dm Am
No, no, no, no.

2.
Gm7
3fr
Dm
If my bod - y was on fire, ooh, you'd
Gm7
3fr
watch me burn down in flames. You said you loved me. You're a li - ar 'cause you
A
A
A
Dm
N.C.
N.C.
N.C.
N.C.
nev - er, ev - er, ev - er did ba - by.
B♭
A
N.C.
But darl - ing I'll still catch a gre - nade

Dm Bb F C Dm Bb
for ya. (Yeah, yeah.) Throw my hand on a blade for ya. (Yeah,

F C Dm Bb F C
yeah.) I'd jump in front of a train for ya. (Yeah, yeah.) You know I'd do an - y - thing

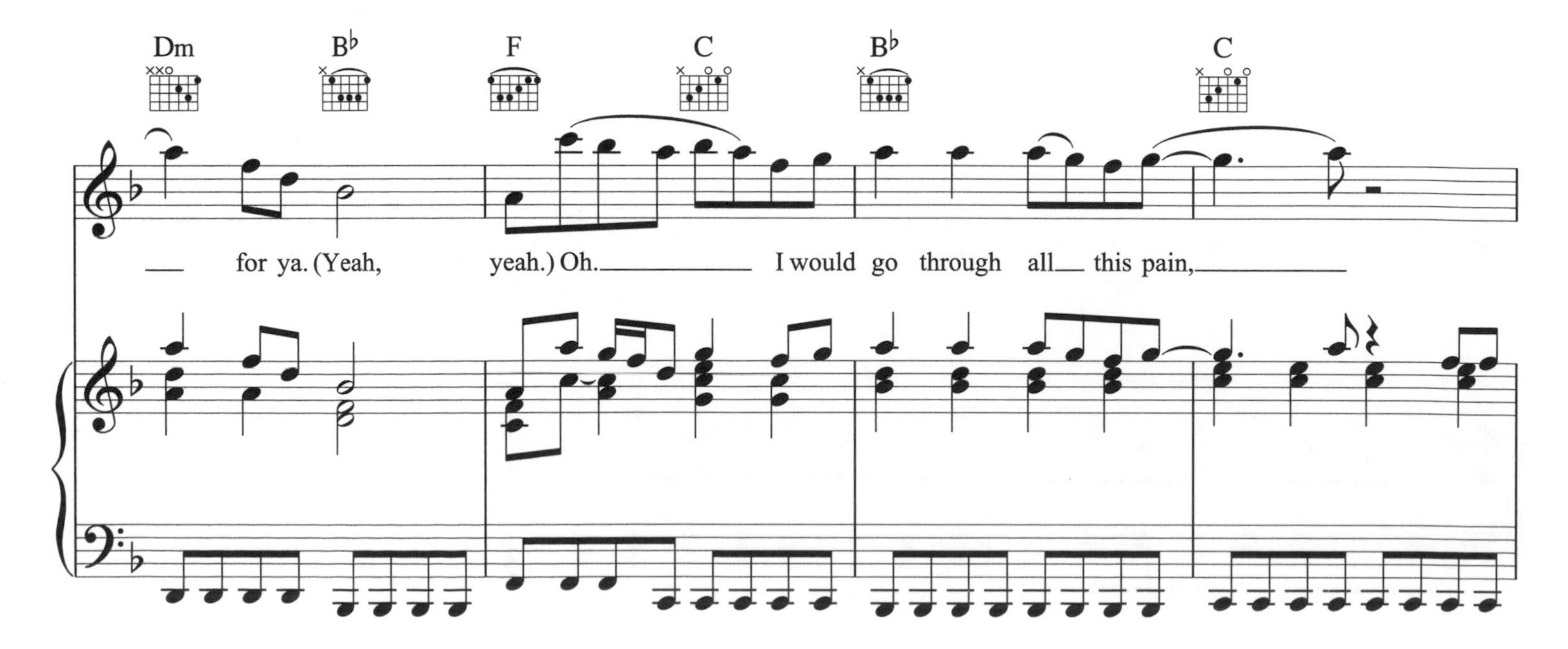
Dm Bb F C Bb C
for ya. (Yeah, yeah.) Oh. I would go through all this pain,

F
A
Dm
C
B♭
take a bul-let straight through my brain. Yes, I would die for you ba - by,
A
N.C.
Dm
but you won't do the same. No, you won't do the same.
Am
Dm
You would-n't do the same. Ooh,
Am
you'll nev-er do the same. No, no, no, no.

Jilted Lovers And Broken Hearts

Words & Music by Daniel Lanois, Brandon Flowers & Stuart Price

Cm
A♭maj7
out there?
(2.) out there?
Some-where I can be - long.
Some-where I can be - long.
E♭
B♭/D
Cm
Man, the cit - y just ain't so kind to - night.
Man, the cit - y just ain't so kind
B♭
to - night.
I need a place to take
And if I had my sus -
Cm
A♭maj7
re - fuge.
- pi - cions,
See, I've been lov - in' you blind.
I kept them out of my heart.

E♭
6fr
B♭
A♭maj7
4fr
I guess I made it hard for me to find
I just wish I would-'ve known right from the start
B♭
that we were caught up in the mid-dle of a worn-out dream. I
that you'd be speak-ing in rid-dles and you'd nev-er con-fide. You know I
E♭
6fr
knew we were in trou-ble, but ba-by, I al-most screamed
knew we were in trou-ble, but hon-ey, I al-most cried
when I saw you danc-
A♭
4fr
E♭/G
3fr
Fm7
-ing on the moon now.

B♭
E♭
6fr
B♭
A♭add9
4fr
I watched him spin you 'round and 'round.
B♭6
Why did you roll your dicc, show your cards? Jil - ted lov -
Cm7
3fr
B♭
A♭
4fr
B♭
- ers and bro - ken hearts. You're fly - ing a - way while I'm stuck
2° You're out on the wind and I'm still wait -
E♭
6fr
B♭
A♭maj7
4fr
here on the ground.
- ing to be found.

1.
2.
B♭
Cm
3fr
2. Is there an - y - one
A♭6
E♭6
Fm
Cm
3fr
A♭6
E♭6
Fm
You

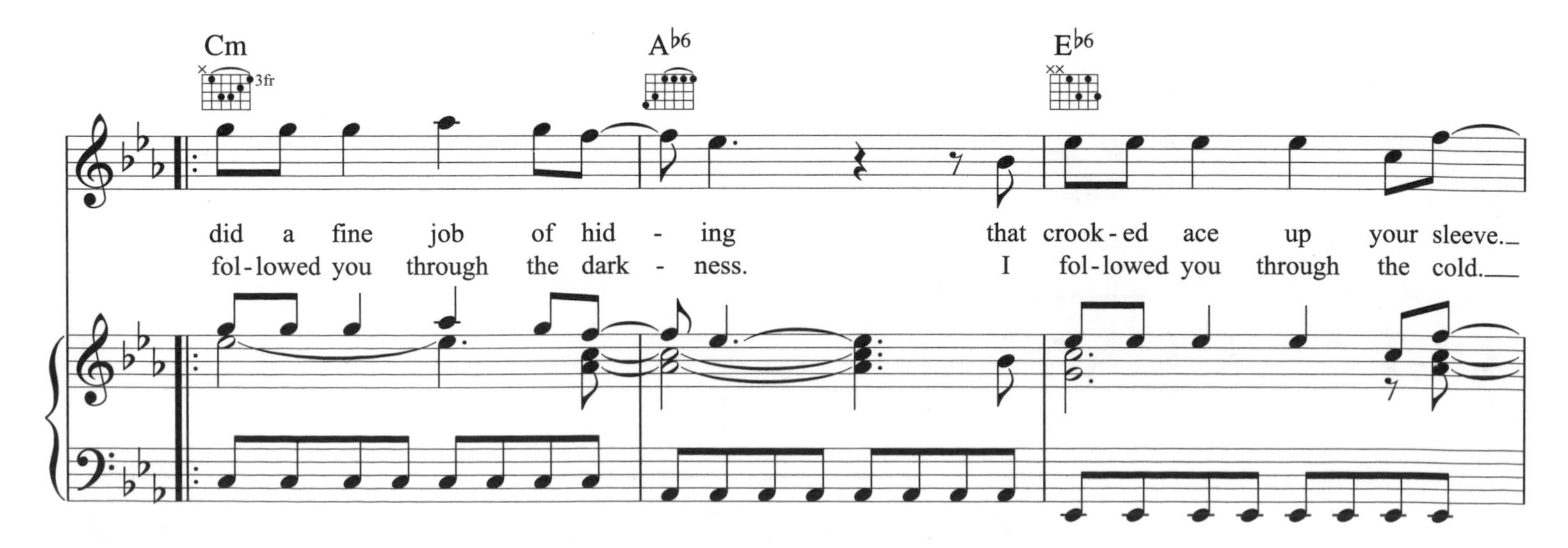
Cm
3fr
A♭6
E♭6
did a fine job of hid - ing that crook - ed ace up your sleeve.
fol - lowed you through the dark - ness. I fol - lowed you through the cold.

Fm
Cm
3fr
A♭6
You dou-bled down my di-rec - tion. You
And wom-an I can tell you one thing, you're gon-na
E♭6
1.
Fm
2.
kiss me on the cheek and leave. I Why did you roll your
wish you could go back and fold.
Drums
B♭6
Cm7
3fr
B♭
dice, show your cards? Jil-ted lov - ers and bro - ken hearts.
A♭
4fr
B♭
1.
E♭
6fr
B♭
You're fly-ing a-way while I'm stuck here on the ground.
2° You're out on a wind, I'm still wait -

2.
A♭maj9
3fr
E♭
6fr
B♭
Why did you roll your
- ing to be found.
A♭maj7
4fr
E♭
6fr
Yeah.
Will I ev-er win?
A♭
4fr
Fm
B♭
On - ly time will tell.
You've got to
E♭
6fr
B♭
A♭
4fr
suf - fer to re-mem-ber how well.
And our i - deas nev -

B♭
Cm
3fr
E♭/B♭
6fr
-er real-ly marched in time.
That's the bot-tom line.
A♭
4fr
B♭sus4
E♭
6fr
B♭
Jilt-ed lov-ers and bro-ken hearts.
A♭add9
4fr
1, 2.
Repeat ad lib.
3.
A♭
4fr

It's OK

Words & Music by Thomas Callaway, Hitesh Ceon, Kim Ofstad, Noel Fisher,
Helgi Hübner, Tshawe Baqwa & Yosef Wolde-Mariam

C
Em
wan-dered a-round after hours of words, and I wait-ed in vain here for weeks.
(2.) once you've had one, you've had ev-'ry wom-an, un-til I lost this leg-
E♭m
The ghost of a girl-friend that's here in my room, I still
-en-dar-y wom-an. Now, I'm sure, that
F/A
G
C
smell her per-fume in my sheets. But that's not her in my bed, no she's
they don't make 'em like her an-y-more. So please, ba-by,

Em
Ebm
6fr
out on the town, and I don't want an - y - one to see there's a tat -
please, lov - er, let's find a way to for - give each oth - er. I've
Dm
F/A
- too of my name on her bod - y, but hon - est - ly, the man hold - ing her hand is - n't me.
got - ten a - round ev - er since you've been gone, but with - out you, I'm still a - lone.
G
N.C.
Oh hon - ey, how could you re - gret me when you can't e - ven for - get me?
Oh, how can you re - gret me when you know you can't for - get me?
Babe, it's

C
F♯m7(♭5)
O. K. to say that you love me;
Dm7
Em7
Fmaj7
Em7
I think of you, still think of
Dm7
Em7
Fmaj7
G
C
you. Oh, it's O. K.
F♯m7(♭5)
to say that you love me; I think of

Dm7
Em7
Fmaj7
Em7
Dm7
Em7
Fmaj7
you,
still think-in' of you.
G
1.
N.C.
Mm.
Mm, mm. 2. I thought that
2.
Dm(add4)
3fr
Am7
I made mis-takes, I'm on - ly hu - - man.

G
Dm
And I am not ashamed to say
Am7
G
Fmaj9
that you
G7(sus4)
G7
are the one.
N.C.
Doo doo doo doo doo doo doo doo doo doo doo, doo doo doo doo doo

Dm7
Em7
Fmaj7
Em7
doo doo doo doo doo doo, doo doo doo doo doo doo doo,
Dm7
Em7
Fmaj7
G
C
doo doo doo doo doo doo. Babe, it's O. K.
F#m7(b5)
to say that you love me; I think of
Dm7
Em7
Fmaj7
Em7
Dm7
Em7
Fmaj7
you, still think of you.

1.
2.
G
C
Babe, it's
Oh, it's O. K.,
F#m7(b5)
oh,
Dm7
Em7
Fmaj7
G
say that you love me.
molto rit.
Fm6
C(add9)
Ooh,
say you love me.
colla voce

If You Wanna

Words & Music by Arni Arnason, Freddie Cowan,
Peter Robertson & Justin Hayward-Young

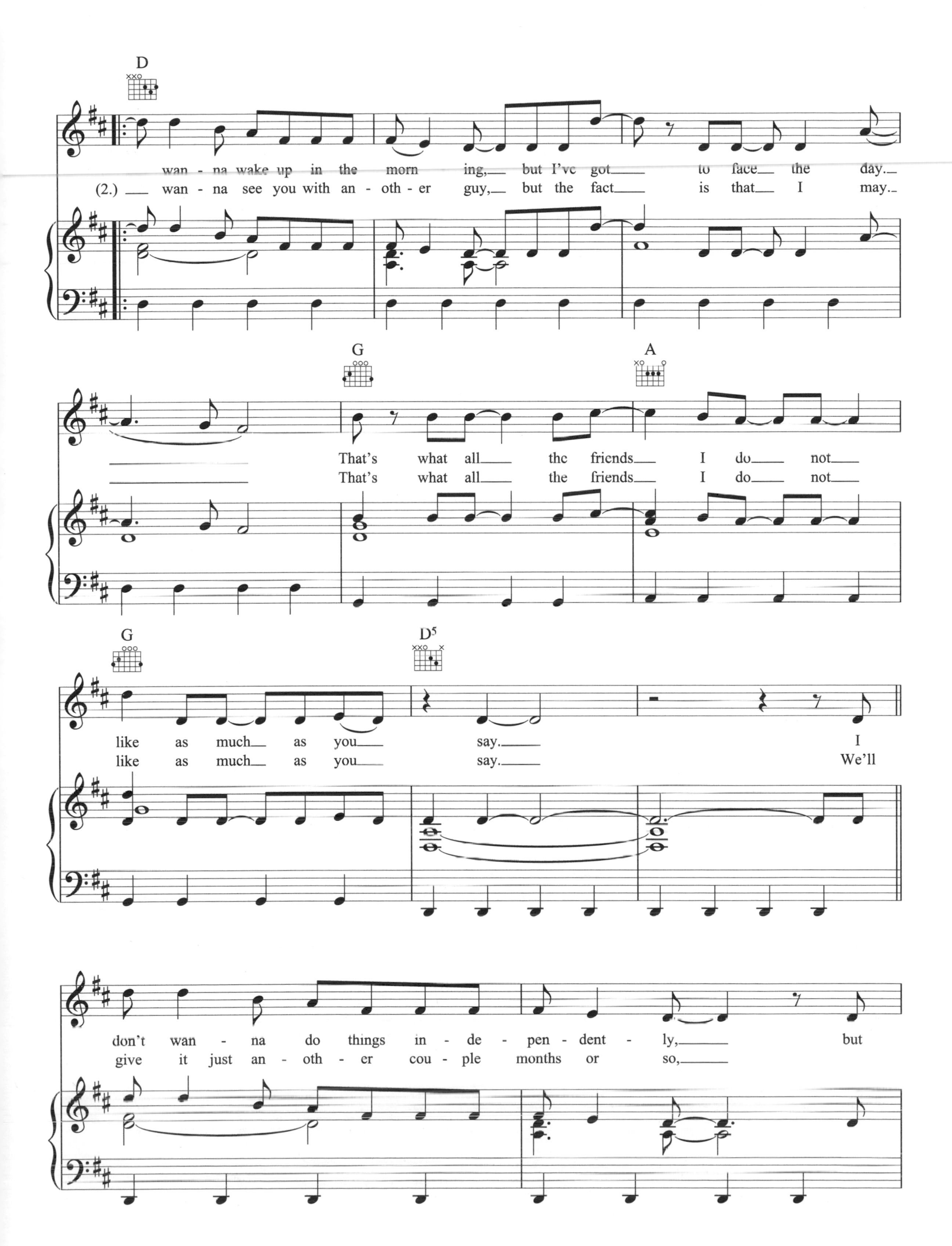
D
wan - na wake up in the morn - ing, but I've got to face the day.
(2.) wan - na see you with an - oth - er guy, but the fact is that I may.
G
A
That's what all the friends I do not
That's what all the friends I do not
G
D5
like as much as you say. I
like as much as you say. We'll
don't wan - na do things in - de - pen - dent - ly, but
give it just an - oth - er cou - ple months or so,

G
I can't make you stay.
then you'll be o - kay.
That's what all the friends
A
G
D5
I do not like as much as you say.
1.
D
But if you wan-na come back it's al-
G
A
D
- right, it's al-right. It's al-right if you wan-na come back. Do you wan-na come back? It's al-

G
A
- right, it's al - right. It's al - right if you wan - na come back to me.

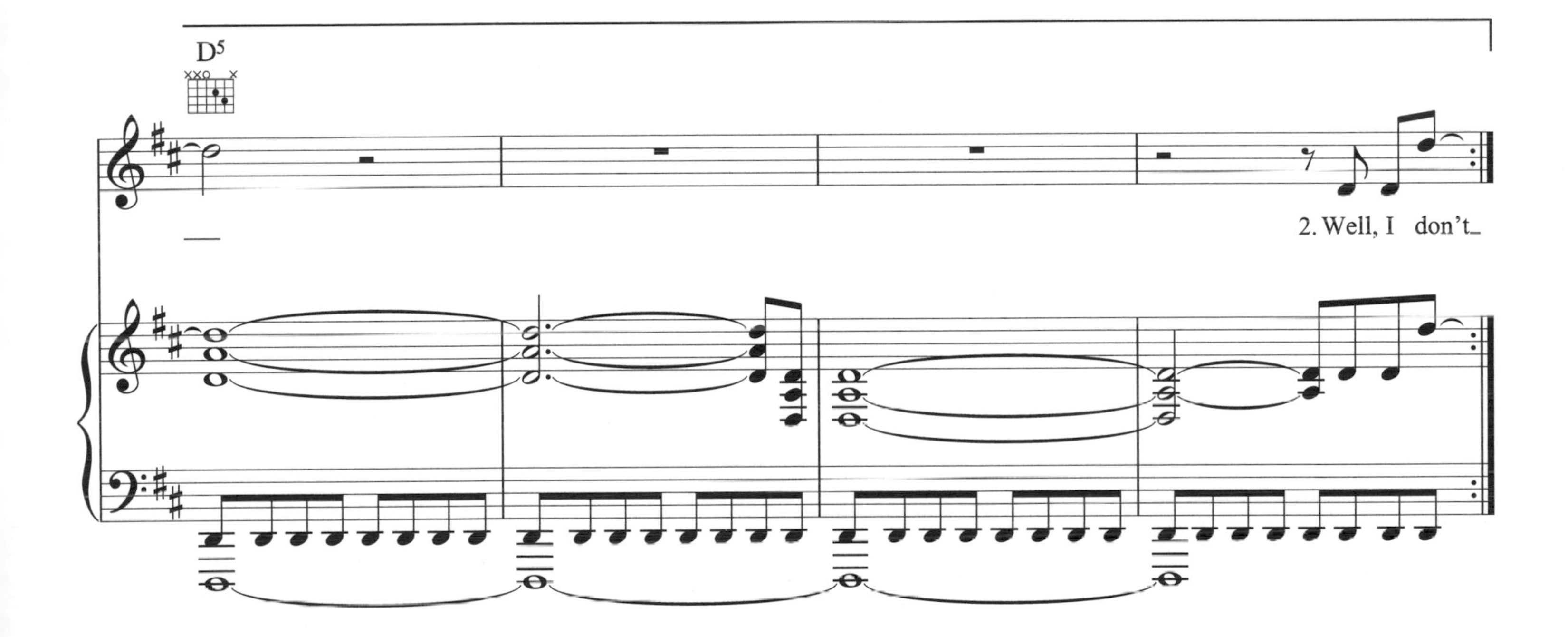
D5
2. Well, I don't

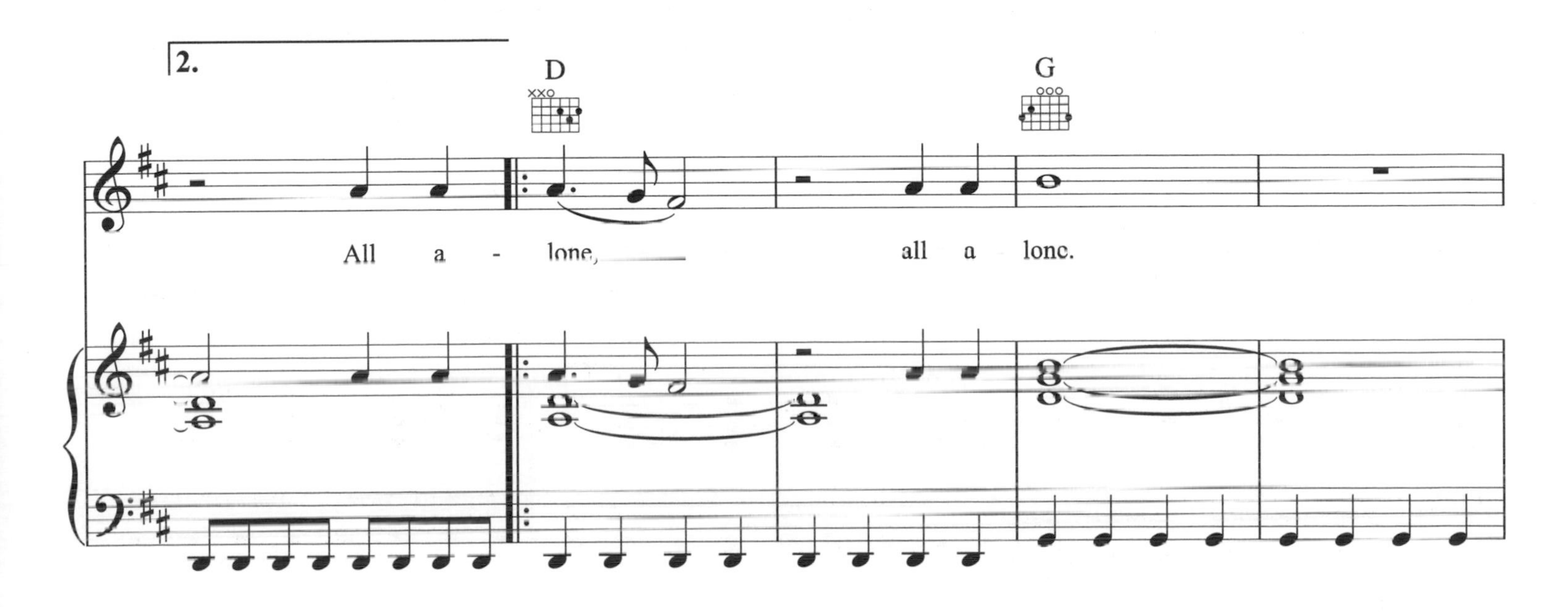
2.
D
G
All a - lone, all a lone.

1.
A
G
D
I, I'm on my own. A-
2.
G
D5
D
I'm on my own. But if you wan-na come back it's al-
G
A
D
-right, it's al-right. It's al-right if you wan-na come back. Do you wan-na come back? It's al-
G
A
-right, it's al-right. It's al-right if you wan-na come back to me.

D
G
A
D
G
A
Oh, do you
D
G
A
wan-na come back? It's al - right, it's al-right. It's al - right if you wan-na come back. Do you
D
G
wan-na come back? It's al - right, it's al - right. It's al - right if you

A
D
wan-na come back. Do you wan-na come back? It's al - right, it's al - right.
G
A
D
It's al - right if you wan-na come back. Do you wan-na come back? It's al -

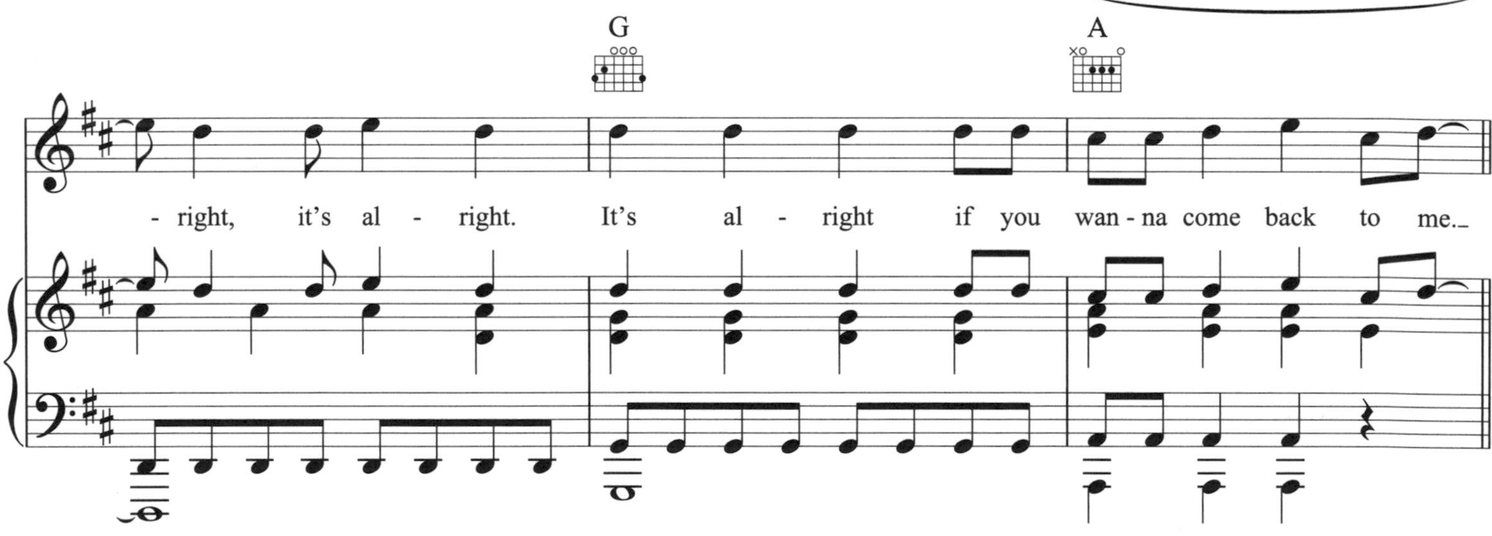
G
A
- right, it's al - right. It's al - right if you wan-na come back to me._

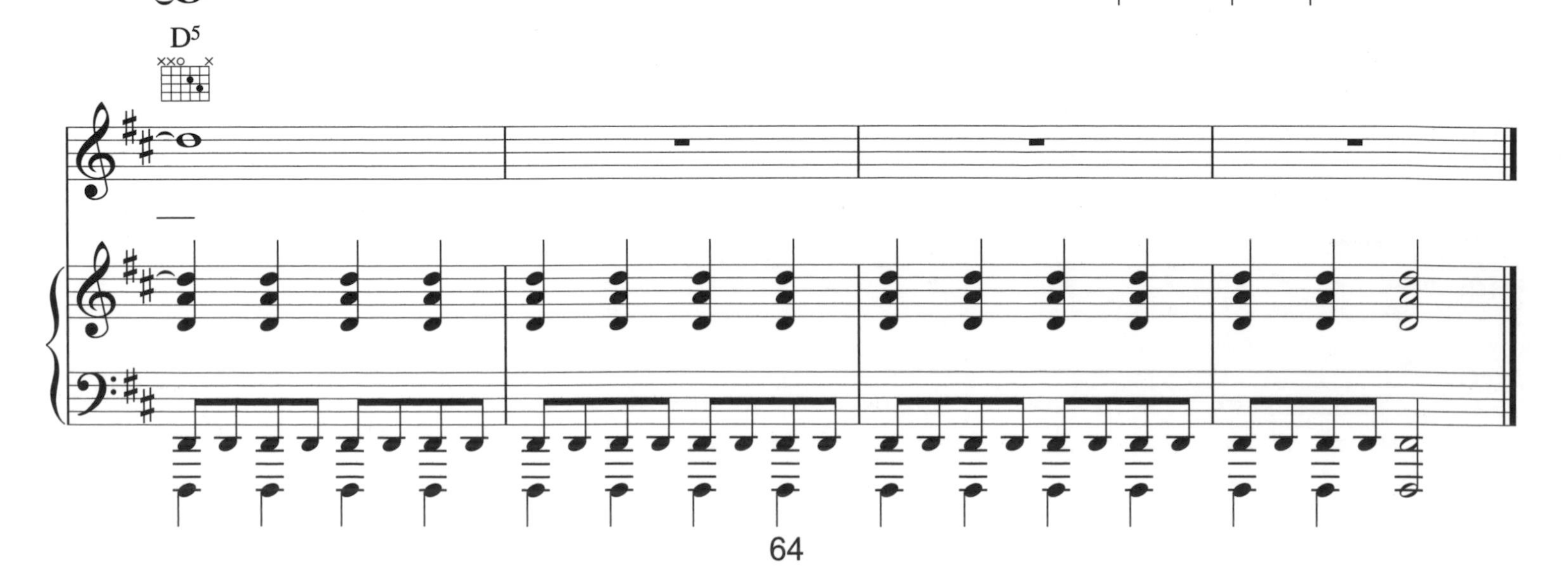
D^5

Kidz

Words & Music by Gary Barlow, Mark Owen, Robbie Williams, Jason Orange & Howard Donald

Dm
Am
B♭
Gm
3fr
Dm
Am
B♭
1. Kings and queens and pre - si - dents,__ min - is - ters__ of
2. Mir - ror, mir - ror on the__ wall__ who's the__ fair - est

Gm
3fr
Dm
Am
go - vern - ments,__ wel - come to the fu - ture__ of your world.__
of them__ all,__ the good, the bad, the ug - ly__ or the beau -

B♭
Gm
3fr
Dm
Through talk - ing__ heads__ that took
- ti - ful?__ Be-cause it's up - hill__ and__ a -

Am
B♭
li - ber - ties the mon - keys learnt to build
-gainst the wind with no - one there to let
Gm
3fr
Dm
Am
ma - chines. They think they'll get to heav - en through the u -
us in. Leave your thoughts and save your - self you fool.
B♭
Gm
3fr
- ni - verse.
B♭
Am6
E7/G♯
They say noth - ing, de - ny ev - 'ry - thing, and make coun - ter
The dag - gers of sci - ence e - volv ing

Am
B♭6
Dm/A
E7/G♯
ac - cu - sa - tions. My friends, my dear, my love, my God.
in - to vi - 'lence. We're not sure where the fall - out blows, but we all know:
A7
Dm
There'll be trou - ble when the kidz come out.
Am
B♭
Gm
3fr
There will be lots for them to talk a - bout.
There'll be trou - ble when the
Dm
Am
B♭
kidz come out, when the kidz come out, when the kidz come out, when the

Gm
3fr
Dm
Am
kidz come out.
(Hey, hey, hey, hey, hey.)
What you look - ing at?
B♭
Gm
3fr
Dm
(Hey, hey, hey, hey.)
You want a bit of that?
(Hey, hey, hey, hey.)
Am
B♭
There will be trou - ble when the kidz come out,
when the
Gm
3fr
Dm
N.C.
kidz come out.
Hey.

B♭
N.C.
Gm
3fr
Out on the
B♭
F
streets to - night they're mak - ing peace to - night, they're mak - ing
A
Dm
peace...
La, la, la, la, la,
1-3.
Am
B♭
Gm
3fr
la, la, la, la, la, la, la, la, la, la, la, la, la, la, la, la, la,

4.
Gm
3fr
Dm
There'll be trou - ble when the kidz come out.
Am
B♭
There will be lots for them to talk a - bout.
Gm
3fr
Dm
Am
There'll be trou - ble when the kidz come out, when the kidz come out, when the
B♭
Gm
3fr
Dm
kidz come out. There'll be trou - ble when the kidz come out.

The Last Dance

Words & Music by Fraser Thorneycroft-Smith & Clare Maguire

D/F♯
Gmaj7
D
A(add11)
G
first man to move me.
You helped me feel a - live.
Bm
A(add11)
G
Got me up from nine to five, oh - ho a - ha.
D
A(add11)
G
D/F♯
I could get through those days.
With you on my mind. Yeah.

G
A(add11)
Bm
Got - ta try, move on, but I prom - ise you I will kiss

D
Gadd9
A
your crown when life takes me down.
I'll save my
Bm
D
G
last dance for you,
my
A
Bm
D
friend.
I'll save my last dance for you,
G
A
Gadd9
my friend.

D A(add11) G Bm A(add11) G
2. An-oth-er face in the crowd.
Oh, peo-ple love to move now.

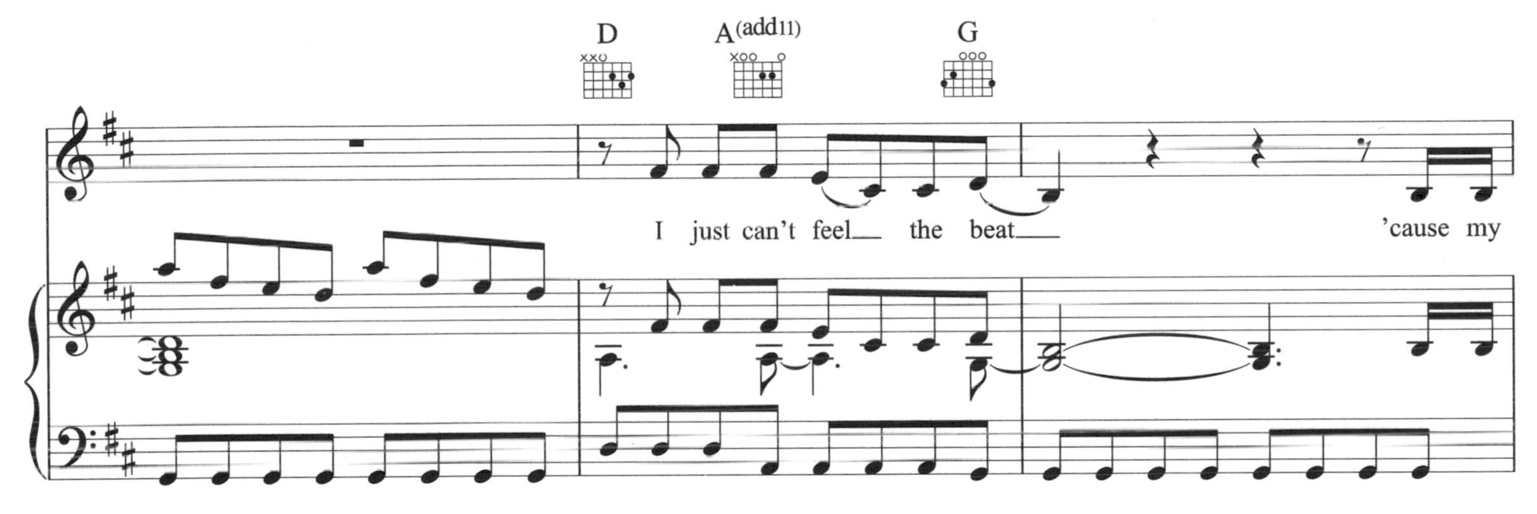
D A(add11) G
I just can't feel the beat 'cause my

D/F# Gmaj7 A(add11)
heart's fall-en out. Yeah. Got-ta try, move, on but I prom-

Bm D Gadd9
-ise you I will kiss your crown when life takes me down.

A
Bm
D
I'll save my last dance for you,
G
A
Bm
my friend. I'll save my last dance
D
G
A
for you, my friend I've got my
Bm
D
G
life in my hands and your love in my heart. I've got my life in my hands and your

A
Bm
D
love in my heart. I'll save my last dance for you,
G
To Coda
A
Gadd9
my friend. And it seems I can live my life
A
Bm7
D
with you as my rhy - thm. Yeah. And I
Em
G
A
D.S. al Coda
know I'll find my feet af - ter the dream - in'. Yeah. Yeah. I'll save my

Coda
G
A
Bm
friend. I've got my life in my hands and your
D
G
love in my heart. I've got my life in my hands and your
A
Bm
love in my heart. I've got my life in my hands and your
D
N.C.
love in my heart. I've got my life in my hands and your love in my heart.

L.I.F.E.G.O.E.S.O.N.

Words & Music by Charlie Fink

♩ = 80
E
A
E/B
A

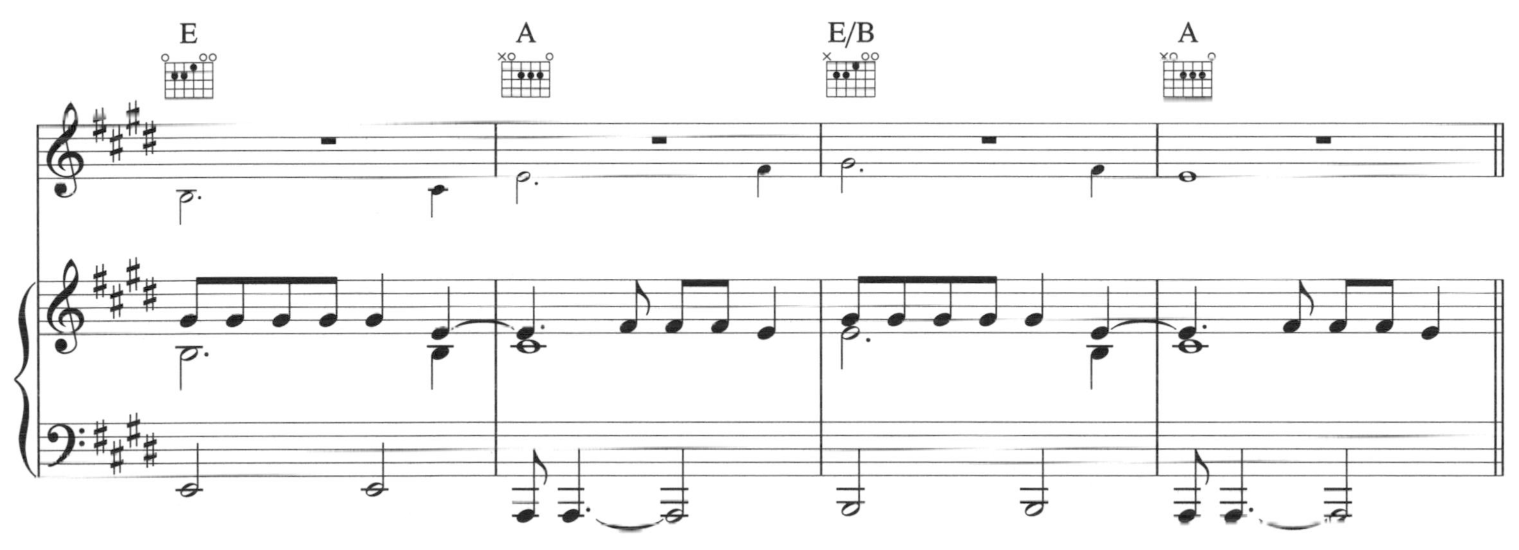

E
A
E/B
A

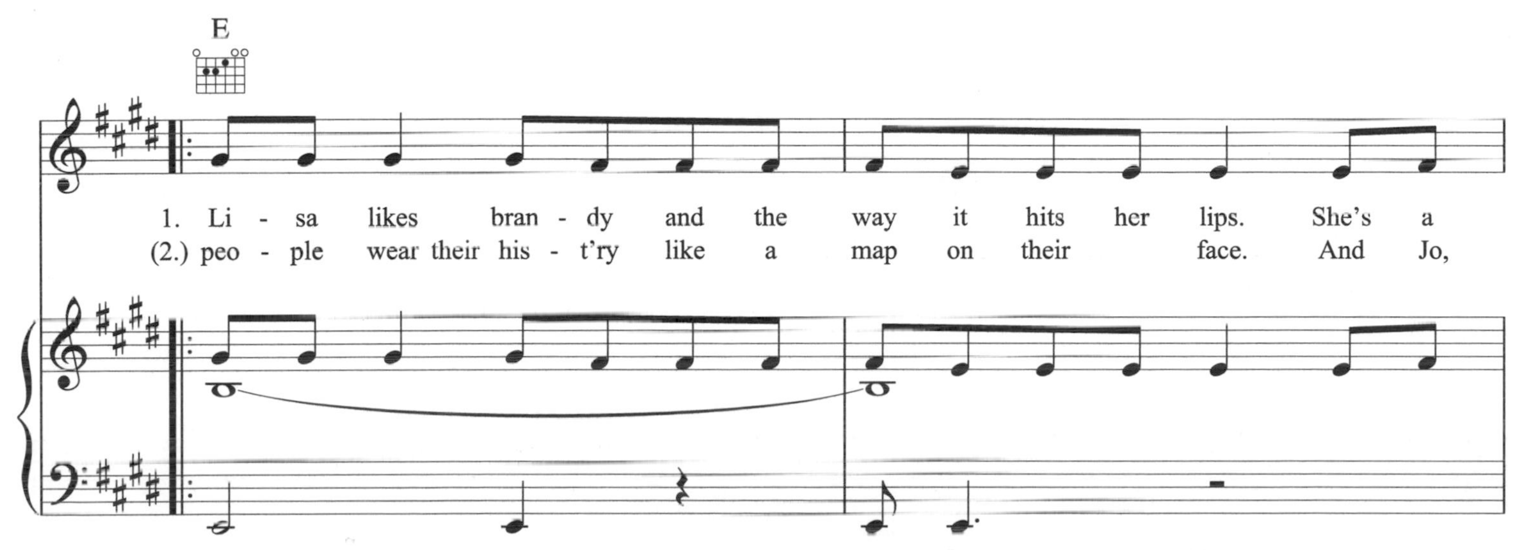

E
1. Li - sa likes bran - dy and the way it hits her lips. She's a
(2.) peo - ple wear their his - t'ry like a map on their face. And Jo,

A
rock 'n' roll sur - vi - vor with pen - du - lum hips. She's got deep brown eyes
he was an ar - tist just liv - ing out a case. But his best work
E
that have seen it all.
was his let - ters home.
Ex -
E
Work - ing at a night club that was called The Av - e - nue, the bar -
-tend - ed works of fic - tion 'bout im - ag - in - 'ry suc - cess. The Cho -
- man used to call her Lit - tle Li - sa, Loon - ey Tunes. She went
- rus girls in ne - on were his clos - est thing to friends but to a

A
E
down
on al - most an - y - one.
writ - er
the truth is no big deal.
F♯m
E
From the hard time liv - ing to the Chel - sea days, from when her
From the hard time liv - ing to the sleep - less nights and the black
A
B
E
hair was sweet blonde till the day it turned grey she said...
and blue bod - y from the week - end fights he'd say...
L. I. F. E. G. O.
A
E/B
A
E. S. O. N. You got more than mon - ey and sense my friend. You got

E
A
E/B
heart and you're go - ing your own way.
A
E
A
L. I. F. E. G. O. E. S. O. N. What you
E/B
A
E
don't have now will come back a - gain. You got heart and you're
A
E/B
1.
A
go - ing your own way.

E
A
E/B
A
E
A
E/B
A
2.
A
2. Some
On my
A
E
C♯m
4fr
B
last night on earth
I won't look to the sky,
just
E
A
E
B
breathe in the air
and blink in the light.
My

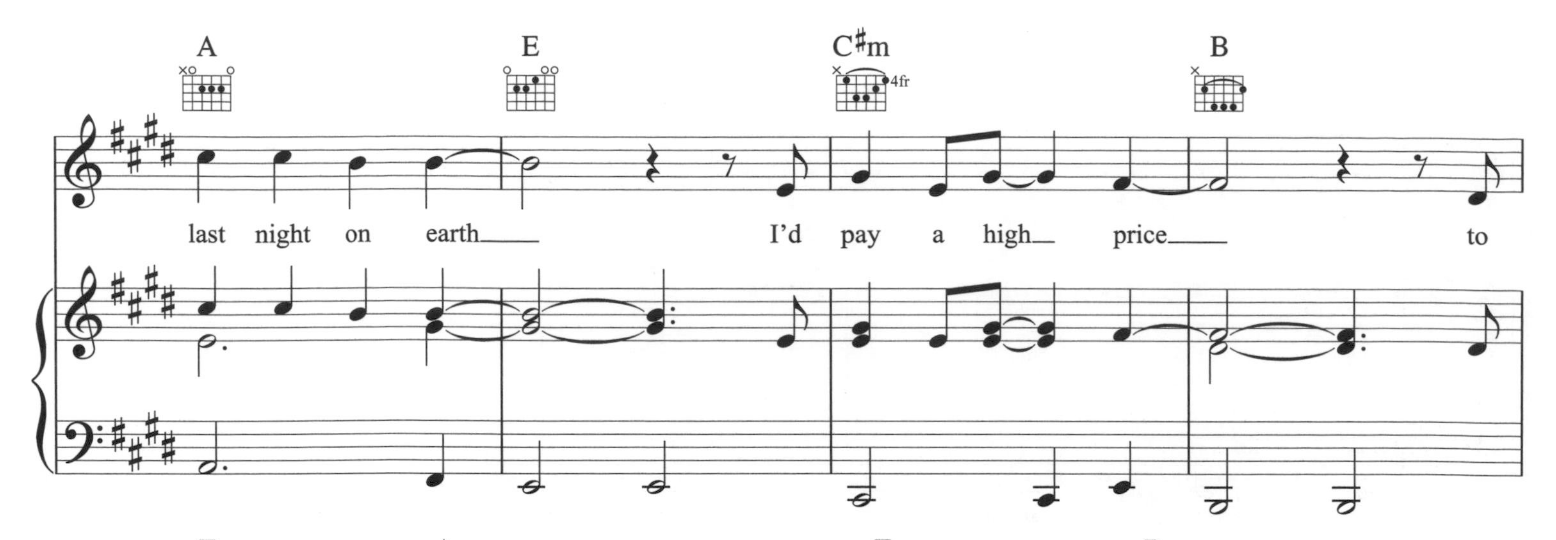
A E C♯m B
4fr
last night on earth I'd pay a high price to

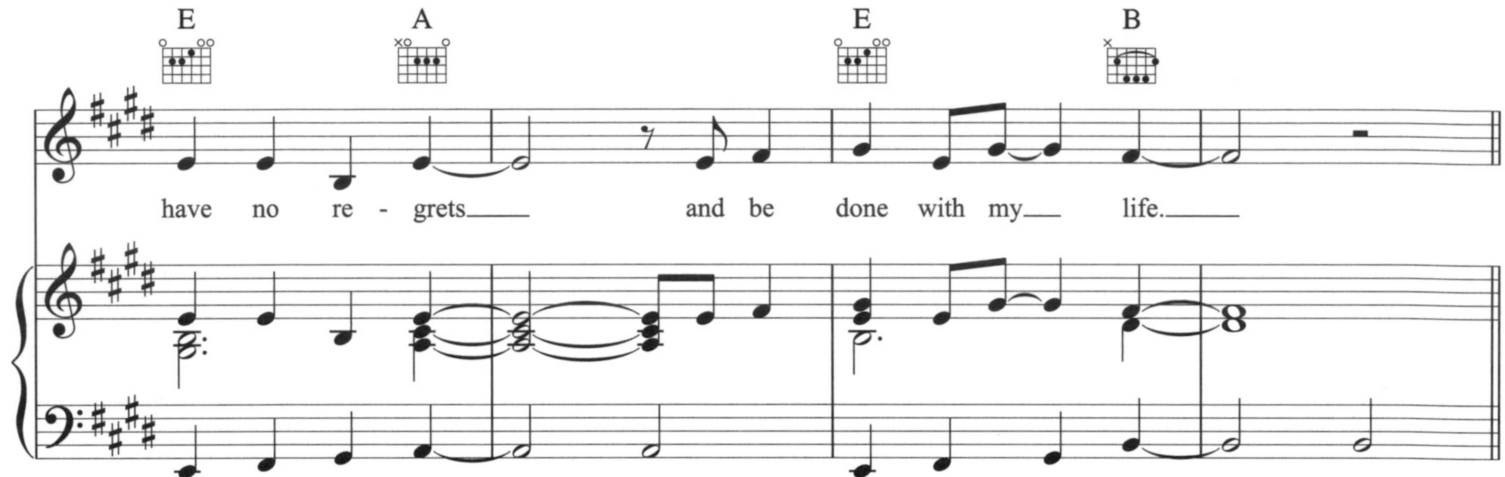
E A E B
have no re - grets and be done with my life.

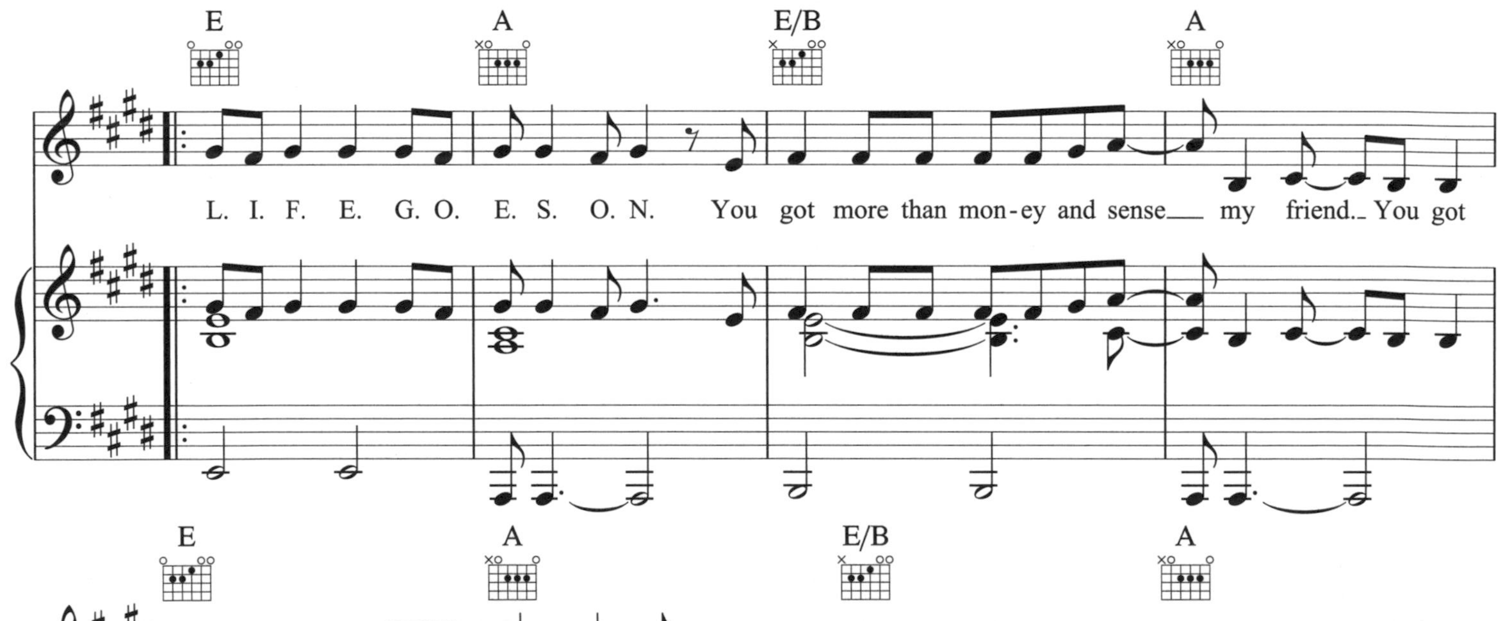
E A E/B A
L. I. F. E. G. O. E. S. O. N. You got more than mon-ey and sense my friend. You got

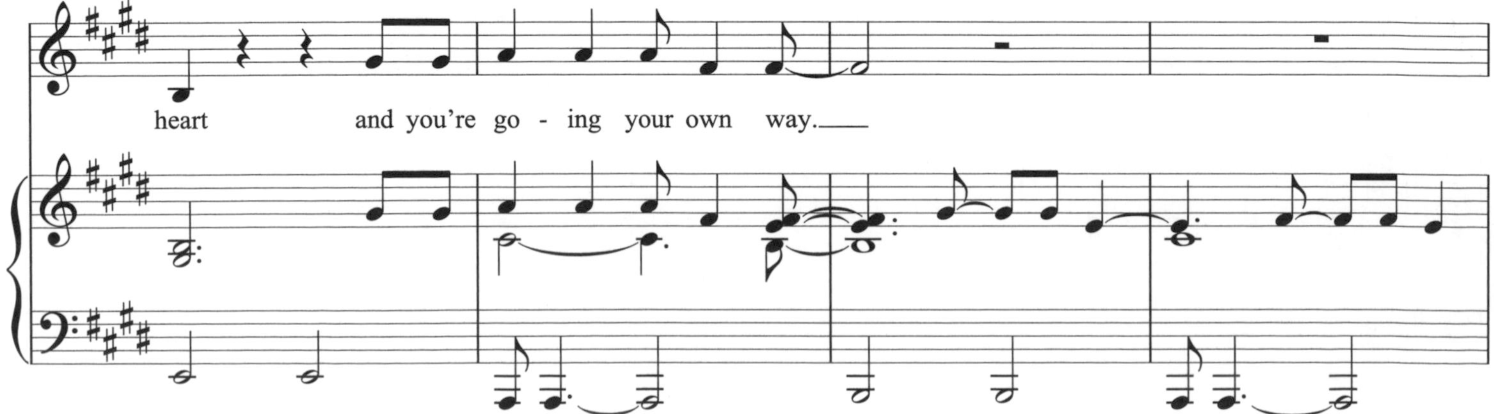
E A E/B A
heart and you're go - ing your own way.

E
A
E/B
A
L. I. F. E. G. O. E. S. O. N. What you don't have now will come back a-gain. You got
heart and you're go - ing your own way.

Love Goes Down

Words & Music by Benjamin Drew, Eric Appapoulay,
Richard Cassell & Tom Goss

♩ = 100
Dm
Am
Gm
Am
Dm
Am
Gm
1. I re - mem - ber when I was young and so were you.
2. I re - mem - ber when I did you wrong, made you cry.
Am
Dm
Am
All of the things we both said
Made you feel so sad I knew I

Gm
Am
Dm
we would nev - er do.
had to a - po - lo - gize.
But look at how times
So I pulled you
Am
Gm
Am
have changed, ba - by:
close ba - by,
You ooh, ooh, know I,
and I laid you down on the bed
Dm
Am
I can nev - er say no, ba - by.
Took off your clothes ba - by,
Gm
N.C.
Dm
B♭
I can on - ly show you how…
girl you know the rest.
My love goes

F
B♭
down,
my love goes

Am
Dm
Gm
Am
Dm
down, down, down.
Yeah ba - by,
sweep your feet right off the ground.
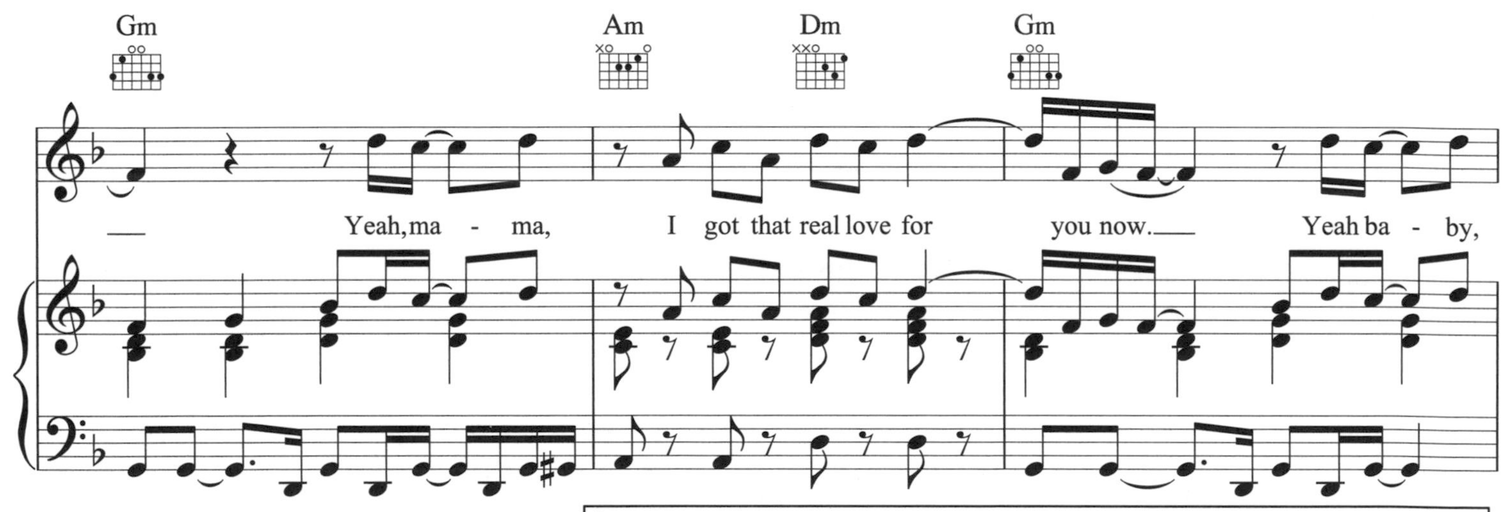
Gm
Am
Dm
Gm
Yeah, ma - ma,
I got that real love for
you now.
Yeah ba - by,

Am
Dm
1.
Gm
know I got that real love for you now.

2.
Gm
Am7
Yeah, yeah, yeah, yeah, hey - ee.
Ba-by, can't you see

Gm7
you're the on - ly one for me - ee?
Whoa, oh - o - oh,

Am7
ooh.
Girl, you know it's true
I'm the on - ly one for
Gm7
Dm
B♭
you ooh, ooh, too, yeah, yeah.
My love goes down,

F
B♭
Am
Dm
whoa, girl, my love goes down, down, down.

Gm
Am
Dm
Gm
Yeah, ba - by, sweep your feet right off the ground. Yeah, ma - ma,

Am
Dm
Gm
Am
Dm
I got that real love for you now. Yeah, ba - by, know I got that real love for you now.

Gm
Am
Dm
Yeah, ooh - hoo, whoa

Gm
Am
Dm
Gm
oh.
Whoa, oh,
ooh - hoo,
yeah.
Yeah,

Am
Dm
Gm
Am
Dm
ooh - hoo,
whoa,
ho.
Whoa, ho,
ooh
hoo,
yeah.

Gm7
Dm

Love The Way You Lie, Part II

Words & Music by Marshall Mathers, Holly Brook
& Grant Alexander

♩ = 90
Gm
3fr
E♭
6fr
B♭
1. On the first page of our sto - ry the fu - ture seemed so bright.
F
Gm
3fr
E♭
6fr
Then this thing turned out so e - vil. I don't know why
B♭
F
Gm
3fr
I'm still sur - prised. E - ven an - gels have their wick -

E♭
6fr
B♭
F
- ed schemes_ and you_ take that_ to new_ ex - tremes._ But you'll

Gm
3fr
E♭
6fr
B♭
al - ways be_ my he - ro_ e - ven though_ you've lost_ your mind._

F
Gm
3fr
E♭
6fr
_ Just gon - na stand there and watch me_ burn,_ but that's all_ right_
B♭
F
Gm
3fr
_ be-cause_ I like_ the way_ it hurts._ Just gon - na stand there and hear me_ cry,_

E♭
6fr
B♭
F
but that's all right because I love the way you lie.
I love the way you lie.
Gm
3fr
E♭
6fr
B♭
Oh,
I love the way you lie.
F
Gm
3fr
E♭
6fr
2. Now there's gra - vel in our voic - es, glass - es shat-
B♭
F
Gm
3fr
- tered from the fight.
In this tug of war, you'll al -

E♭
6fr
B♭
F
N.C.
- ways win e - ven when I'm right. 'Cause you feed

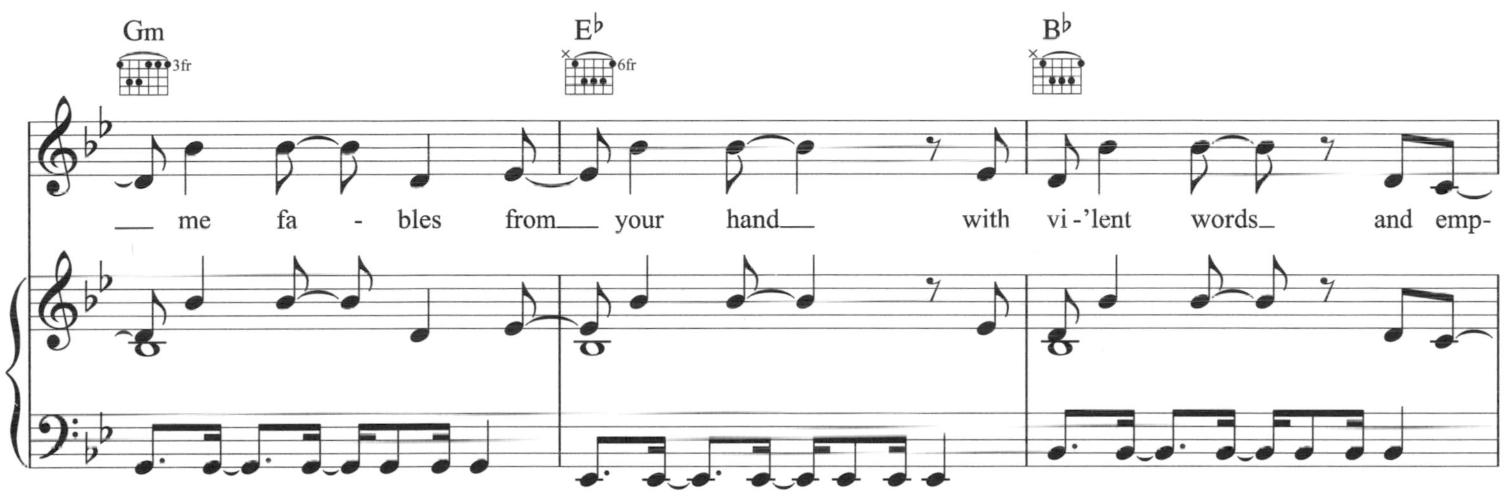
Gm
3fr
E♭
6fr
B♭
me fa - bles from your hand with vi - 'lent words and emp -

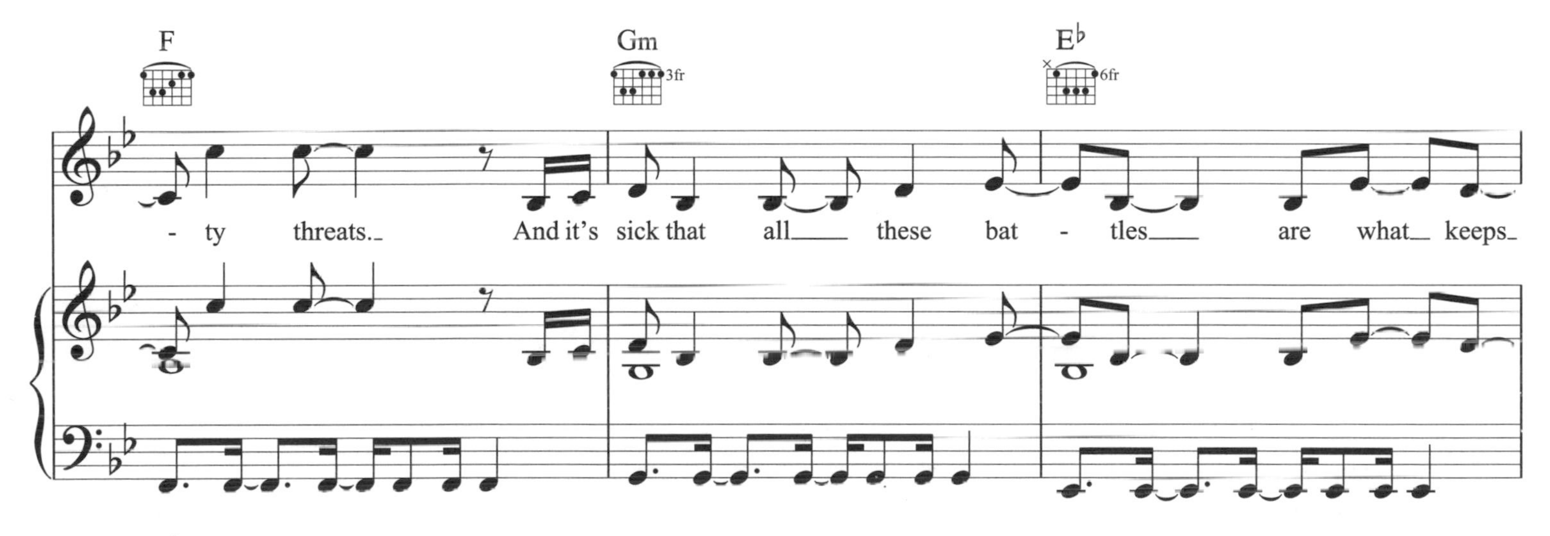
F
Gm
3fr
E♭
6fr
- ty threats. And it's sick that all these bat - tles are what keeps

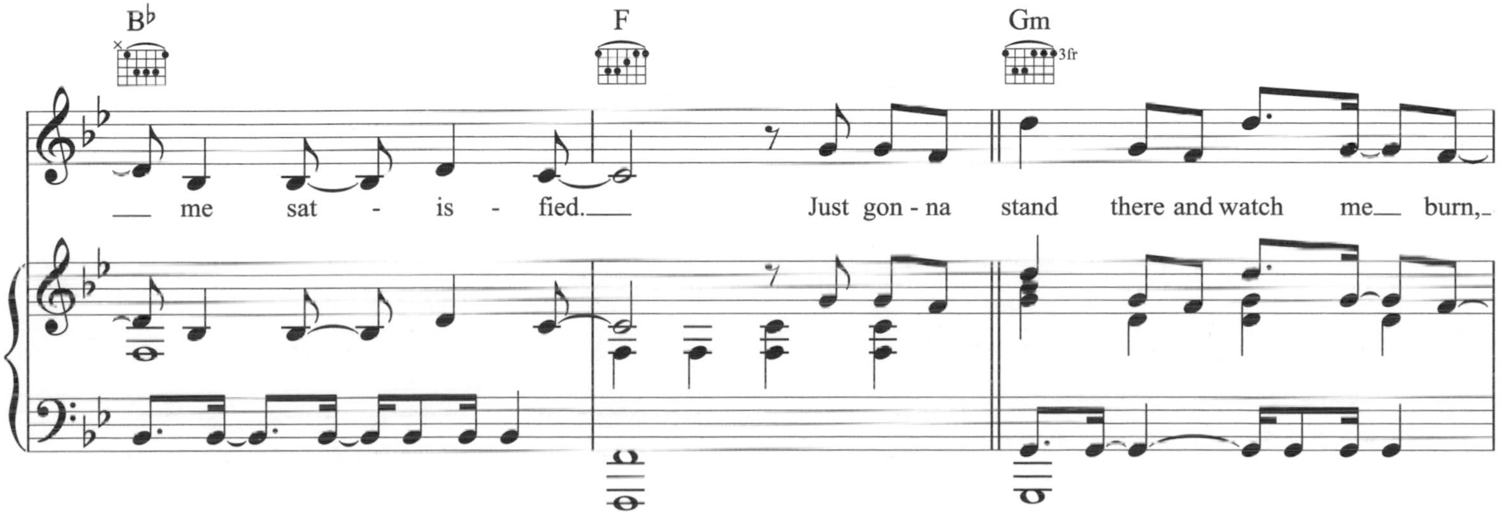
B♭
F
Gm
3fr
me sat - is - fied. Just gon - na stand there and watch me burn,

E♭
6fr
B♭
F
but that's all right be-cause I like the way it hurts.
Just gon-na
Gm
3fr
E♭
6fr
B♭
stand there and hear me cry,
but that's all right be-cause I love the way you lie.
F
Gm
3fr
E♭
6fr
I love the way you lie.
Oh,
I love the way you lie.
B♭
F
F
Oh.
So may-be I'm a

Gm
B♭
Gm
3fr
ma - so - chist.
I try to run,
but I don't wan - na ev - er leave

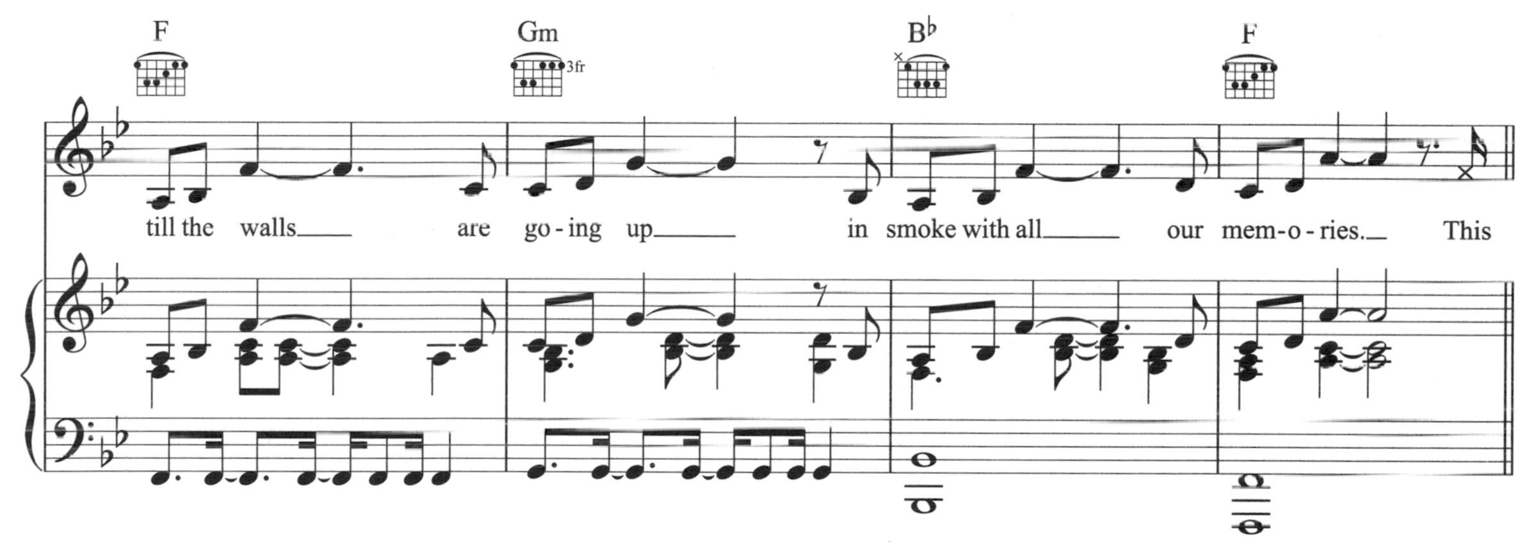

F
Gm
B♭
F
3fr
till the walls
are go - ing up
in smoke with all
our mem - o - ries.
This

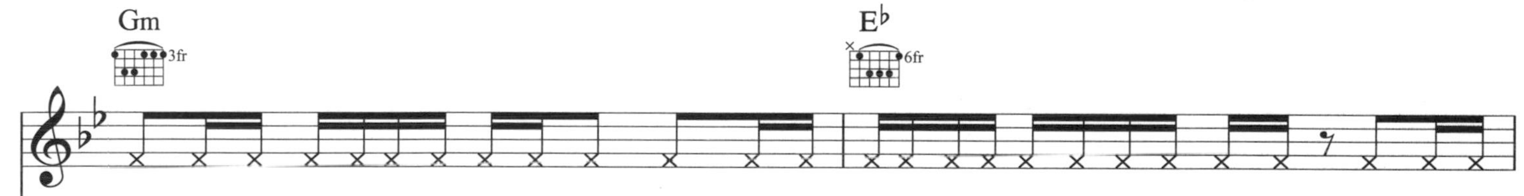

Gm
E♭
3fr
6fr
morn - ing, you wake, a sun ray hits your face. Smeared make-up
as we lay in the wake of des - truc - tion. Hush ba - by,

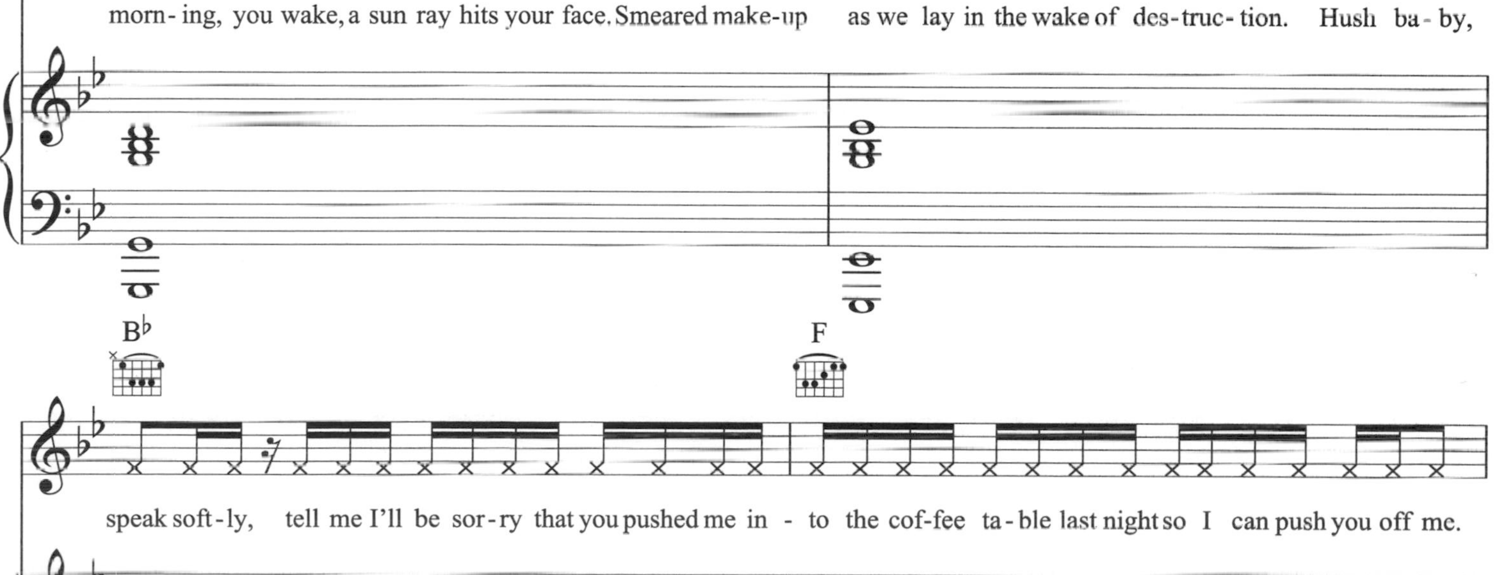

B♭
F
speak soft - ly, tell me I'll be sor - ry that you pushed me in - to the cof - fee ta - ble last night so I can push you off me.

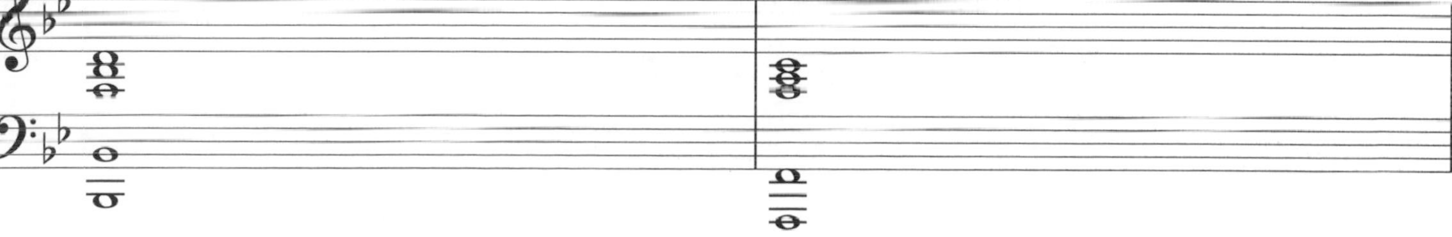

Gm
3fr
E♭
6fr
Try and touch me so I can scream at you not to touch me. Run out the room and I'll fol-low you like a lost pup-py.
B♭
F
Ba-by, with-out you, I'm noth-ing, I'm so lost, hug me. Then tell me how ug-ly I am, but that you'll al-ways love me.
Gm
3fr
E♭
6fr
Then af-ter that, shove me, in the af-ter-math of the des-truc-tive path that we're on, two psy-cho-paths. But we
B♭
F
N.C.
know that no mat-ter how man-y knives we put in each oth-er's backs that we'll have each oth-er's backs. 'Cause we're that luck y.

Gm
Eb
To-geth-er we move moun- tains, let's not make_ moun-tains out of mole hills. You hit me twice, yeah, but who's count-ing?
Bb
I may have hit you three times,___ I'm star - ting to lose count. But
F
Gm
to-geth- er, we'll live for-ev- er, we found the youth foun tain. Our love is cra-zy, we're nuts,_ but I re-fused couns-'ling.
Eb
This house is too huge, if you move out I'll burn all two thou - sand

B♭
square feet of it to the ground. Ain't sh** you can do a - bout it.
F
'Cause with you I'm in my f***- in' mind, with - out you, I'm out it.
Just gon - na
Gm
3fr
E♭
6fr
B♭
stand there and watch me burn, but that's all right be-cause I like the way it hurts.
F
Gm
3fr
E♭
6fr
Just gon-na stand there and hear me cry, but that's all right

B♭
F
be - cause I love the way you lie.
I love the way you lie.
Gm
3fr
E♭
6fr
B♭
I love the way you lie.
F
Gm
3fr
E♭
6fr
I love the way you lie.
B♭
F
N.C.
I love the way you lie.

Mr Medicine

Words & Music by John Beck, Steven Chrisanthon
& Eliza Caird

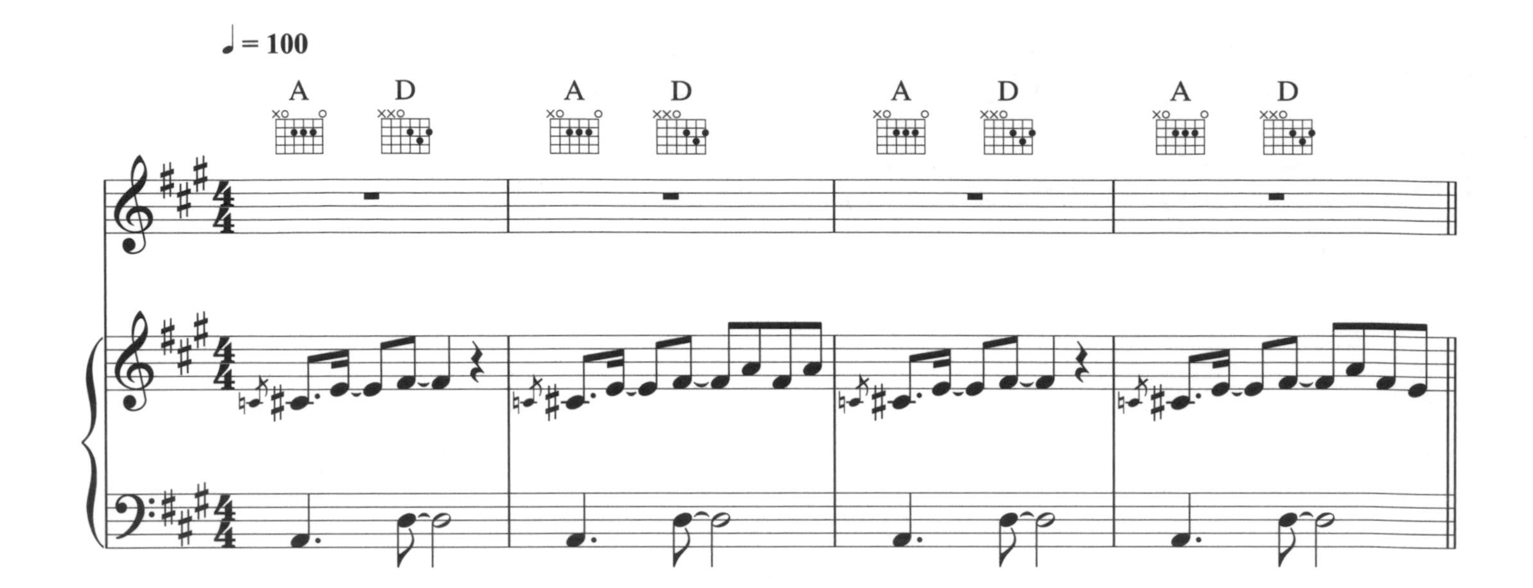
♩ = 100
A
D
A
D
A
D
A
D

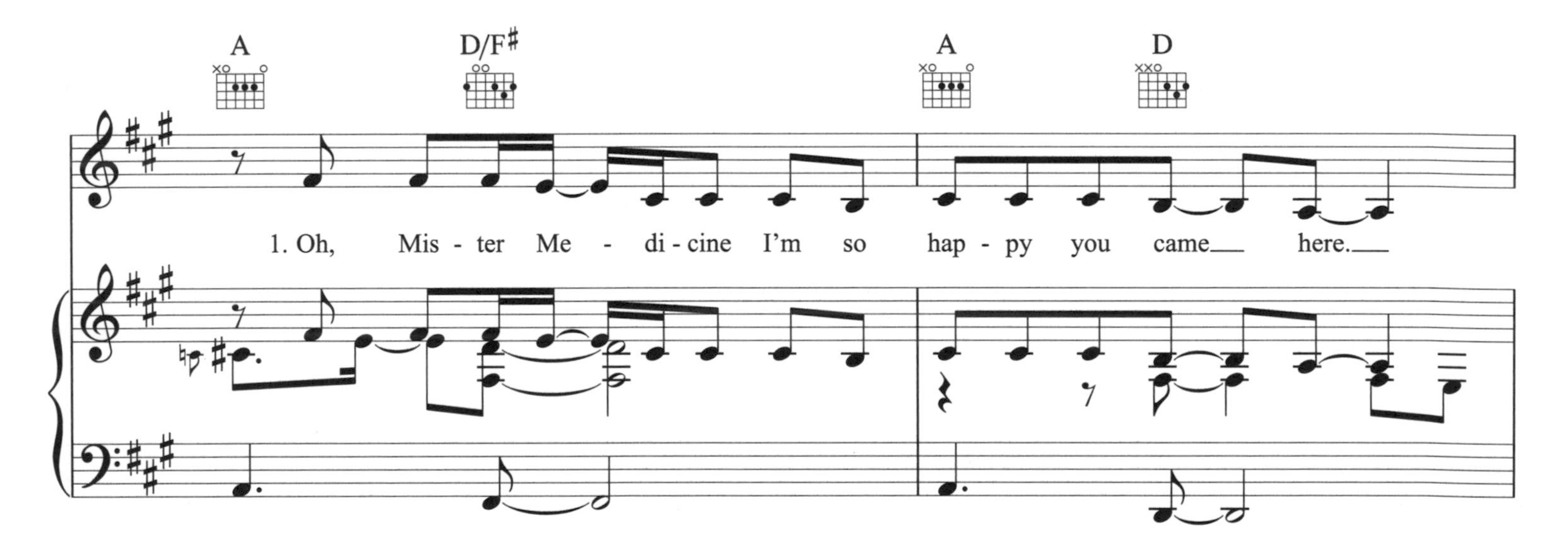
A
D/F♯
A
D
1. Oh, Mis - ter Me - di - cine I'm so hap - py you came here.

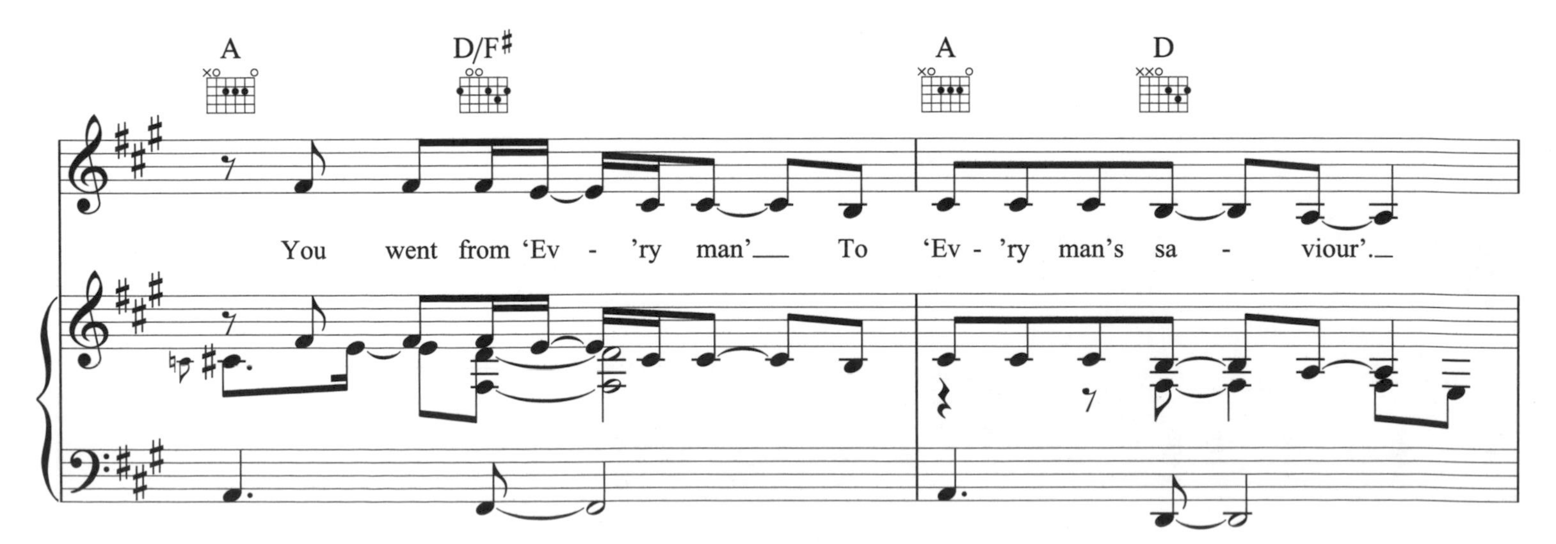
A
D/F♯
A
D
You went from 'Ev - 'ry man' To 'Ev - 'ry man's sa - viour'.

A
D/F♯
A
D
When we all took to E - ver - est we were look - king for change, sir.
F♯m
D
A
E
More doors will start to o - pen, this cy - cle has now been bro - ken.
A
D
A
D
First job, when you get up: there's a pile of dirt - y laun - dry.
A
D
A
D
I know you'll clean it up, you're the man to do it for me.

G
A
I trust your judg - ment, I like the things you say.
𝄋 And then I saw that the pa - tient has im - proved.
G
E
It's com - mon sense I could take three times a day.
To call in sick has be - come a lame ex - cuse.
A D A D A D
Oh, Mis - ter Me - di - cine, I will take an - y - thing. What do you
A Dsus2 A D A D
re - com - mend? Oh, Mis - ter Me - di - cine, I need my vi -

A
D
A
Dsus2
To Coda
ta - mins. Will I feel bet - ter then?
A
D
A
D
A
D
2.Oh, Mis-ter Me - di-cine I feel so much bet - ter. My friend's a pes - si-mist, but
A
D
A
D
you still im - press her. If you need ev - i - dence, then I'll
A
D
F♯m
D
A
E
D.S. al Coda
write you a let - ter. I'll lick the stamp and post it just so that you can no - tice.

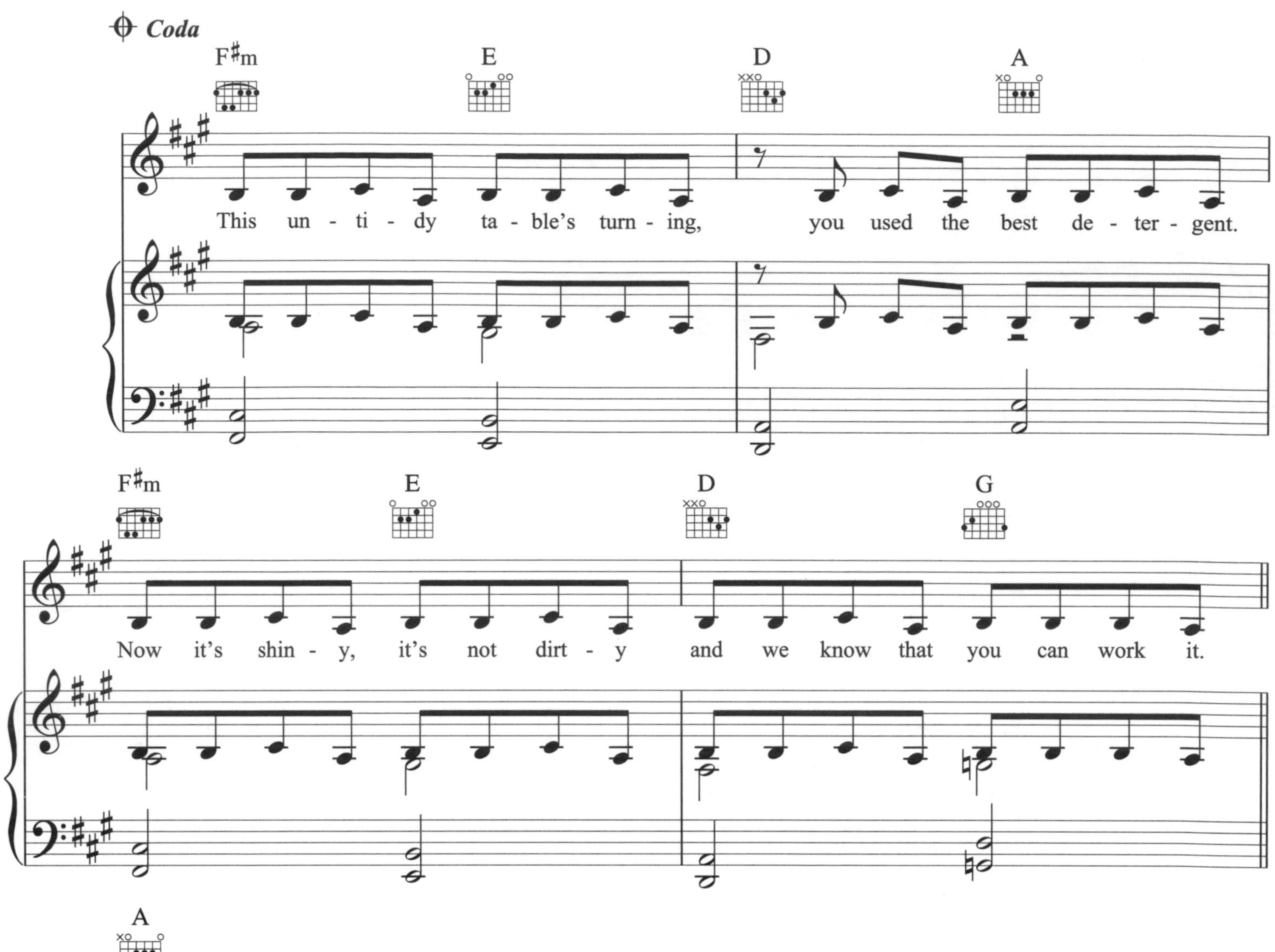
Coda
F♯m
E
D
A
This un - ti - dy ta - ble's turn - ing, you used the best de - ter - gent.
F♯m
E
D
G
Now it's shin - y, it's not dirt - y and we know that you can work it.

A
Oh, Mis - ter Me - di - cine, oh, Mis - ter Me - di - cine.

Oh, Mis - ter Me - di - cine, oh, Mis - ter Me - di - cine.

A D A D A D
Oh, Mis-ter Me - di-cine, I will take an - y-thing. What do you
A Dsus2 A D A D
re - com - mend? Oh, Mis-ter Me - di - cine, I need my vi -
A D A Dsus2
- ta - mins. Will I feel bet - ter then?
A D A D
Oh, Mis - ter Me - di - cine, oh, Mis - ter Me - di - cine.

A
D
Oh, Mis - ter Me - di - cine, oh, Mis - ter Me - di - cine.
Oh, Mis - ter Me - di - cine, I will take an - y - thing.
What do you re - com - mend?
Oh, Mis - ter Me - di - cine, I need my vi - ta - mins.
Will I feel bet - ter then?

Never Say Never

Words & Music by Thaddis Harrell, Nasri Atweh, Justin Bieber, Adam Messinger,
Jaden Smith & Omarr Rambert

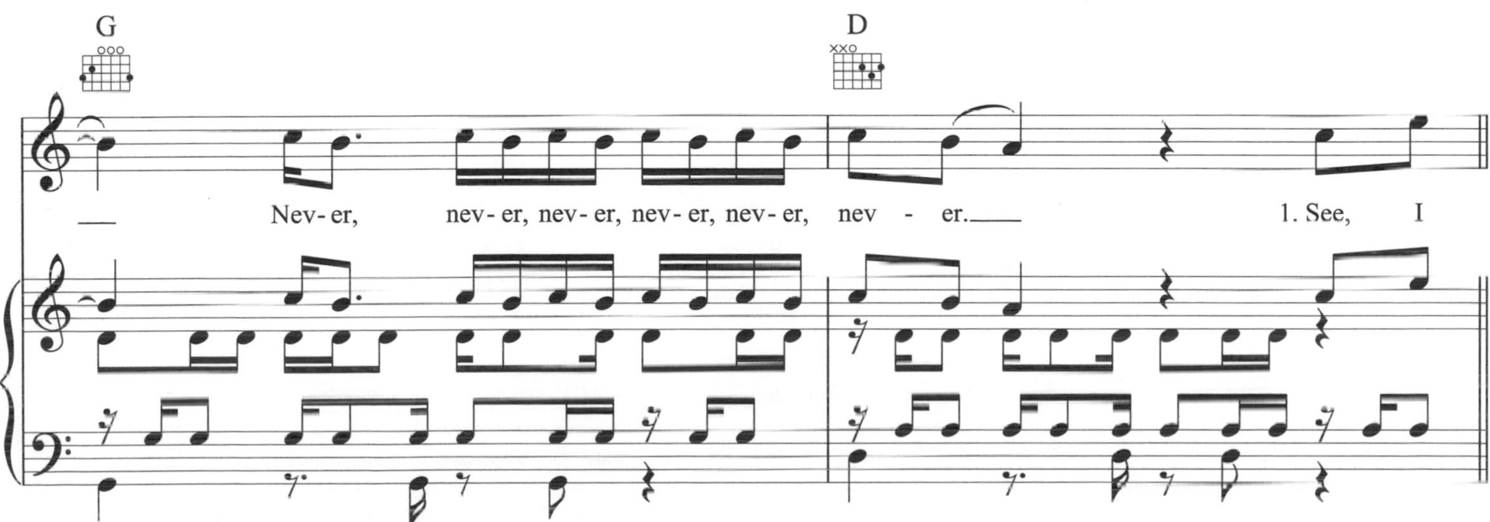

Am
C
never thought that I could walk through fire.
I
G
D
never thought that I could take the burn.
I
Am
C
never had the strength to take it high - er,
Un -
G
D
-til I reached the point of no re - turn.
And there's

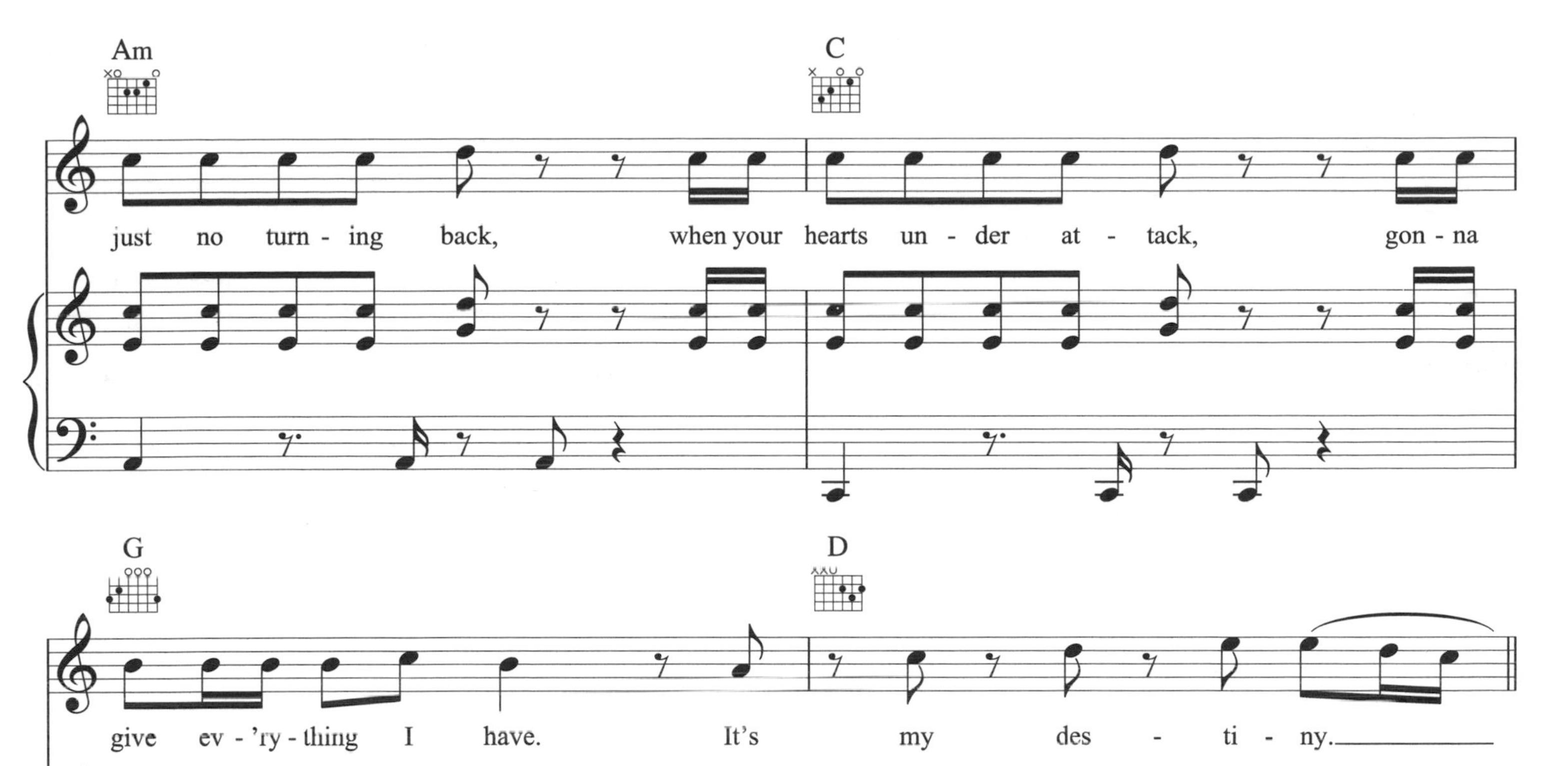
Am
C
just no turn - ing back, when your hearts un - der at - tack, gon - na
G
D
give ev - 'ry - thing I have. It's my des - ti - ny.

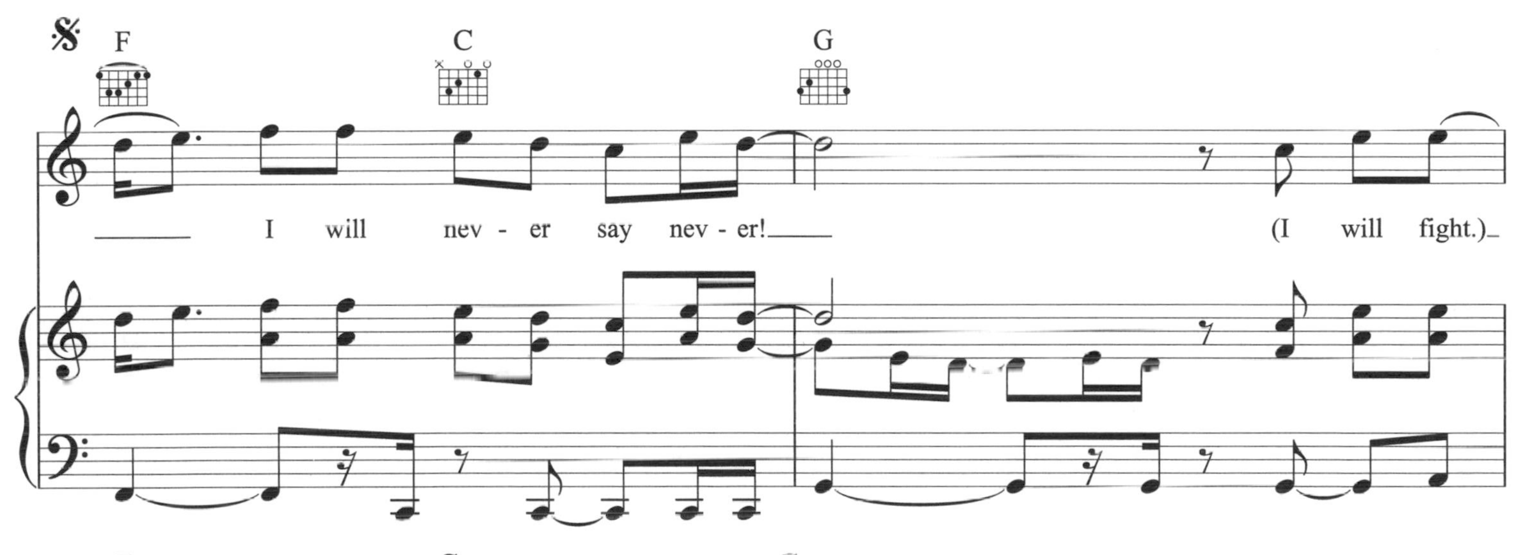
F
C
G
I will nev - er say nev - er! (I will fight.)

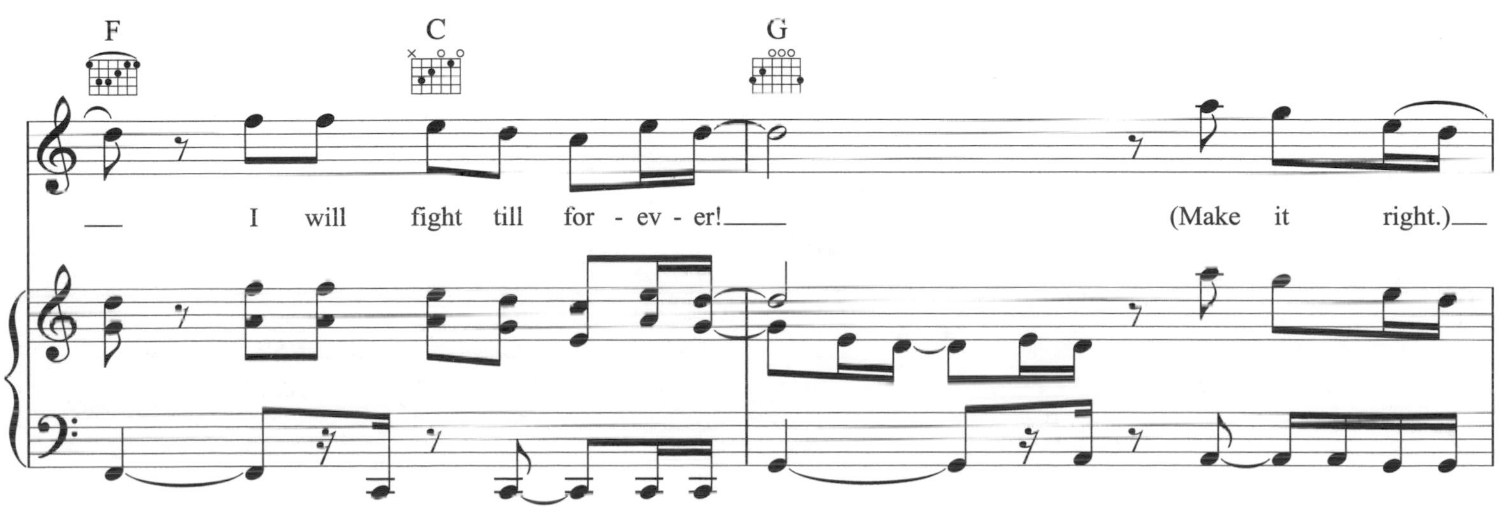
F
C
G
I will fight till for - ev - er! (Make it right.)

F
C
G
Am
Whenever you knock me down, I will not stay on the ground.
D7sus2
To Coda
Pick it up, pick it up, pick it up, pick it up, up, up and never say never.
Am
C
N - never say never. N - never say never.
G
D
N - never say never. Never say it, never never say. 2. I

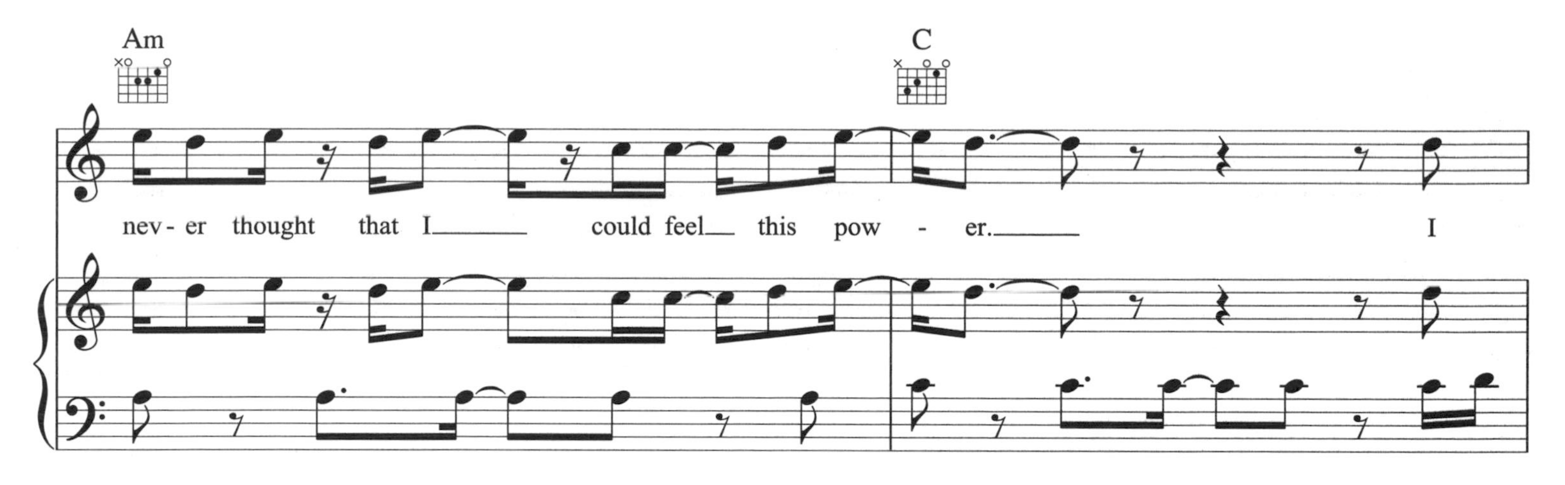
Am
C
nev - er thought that I could feel this pow - er. I

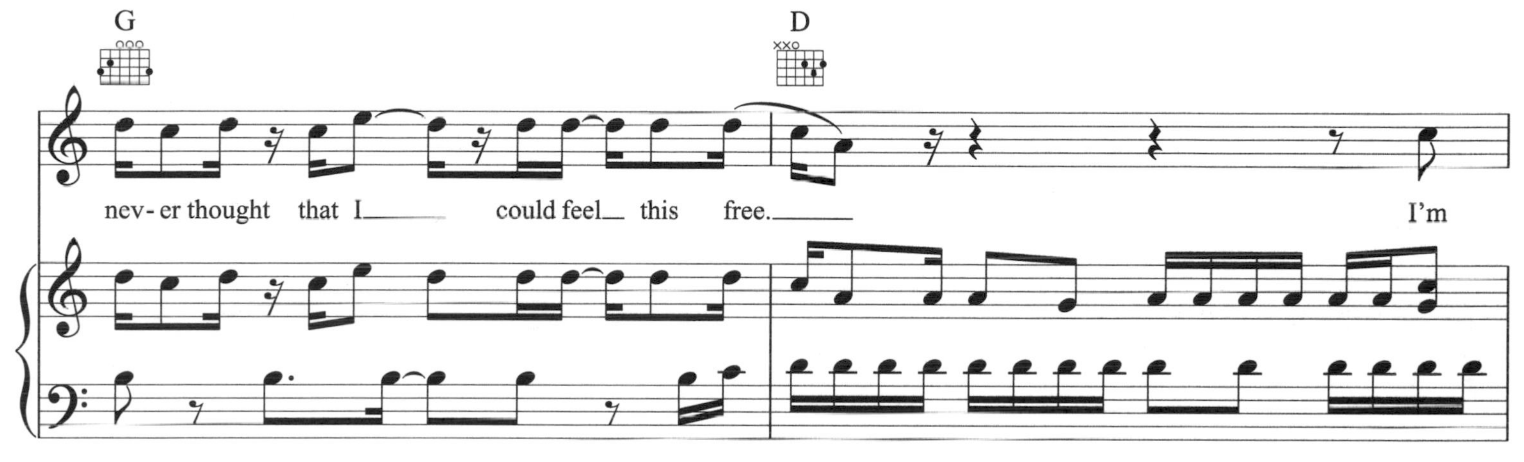
G
D
nev - er thought that I could feel this free. I'm

Am
C
strong e - nough to climb the high - est tow - er. And I'm
G
D
fast e - nough to run a - cross the sea. And there's

Am
G
C
just no turn - ing back, when your heart's un - der at - tack, gon - na

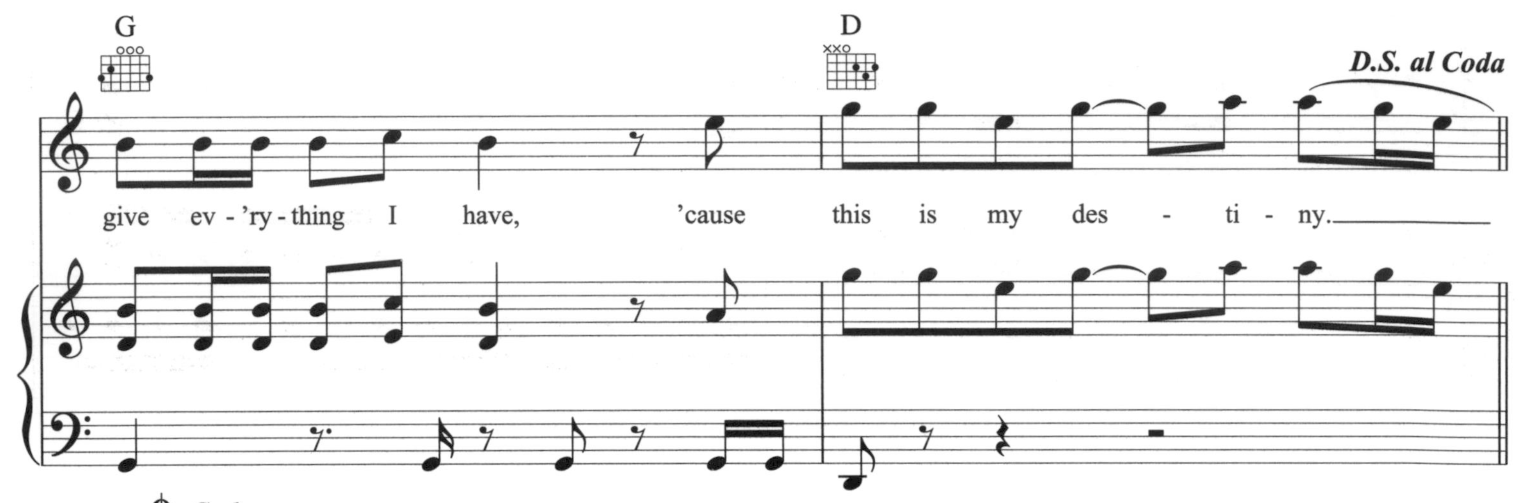
G
D
D.S. al Coda
give ev - 'ry - thing I have, 'cause this is my des - ti - ny.

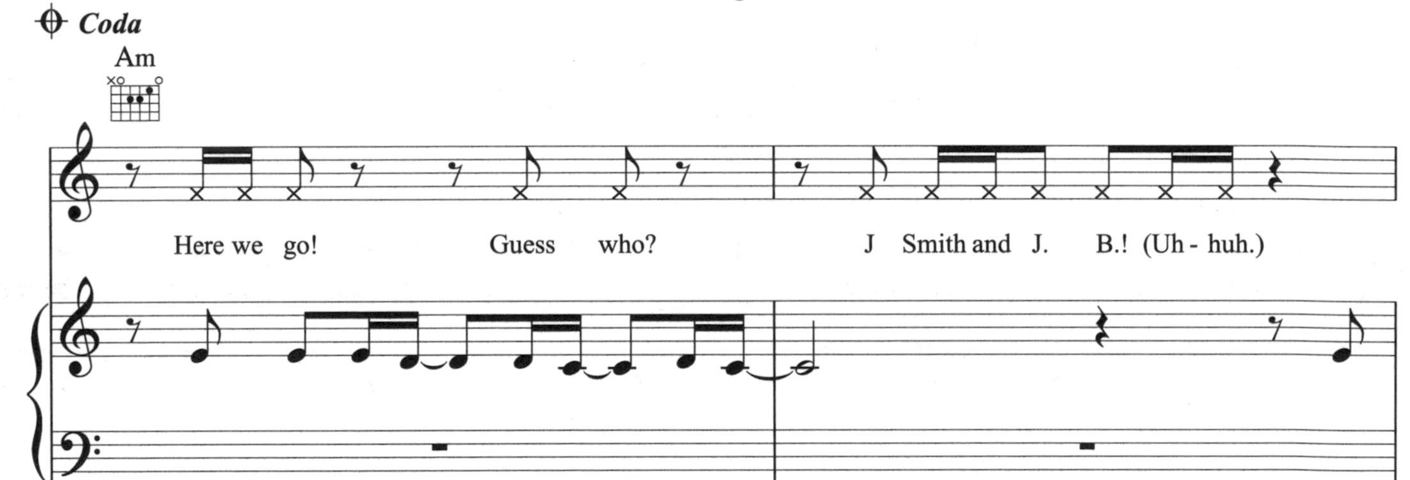
Coda
Am
Here we go! Guess who? J Smith and J. B.! (Uh - huh.)

3
3
3
3
I can han - dle him, hold up, right! I can han - dle him. Now

Am
he's big-ger than me, tall-er than me, and he's old-er than me, and strong-er than me. And
his arm's a lit-tle bit long-er than me, but he ain't on a J. B. song with me. I be
try'n' to chill, they be try'n' to side with the thrill, no pun in-ten-ded was raised by the pow-er of Will. Like
Luke with the Force if push comes to shove, like Ko-be in the forth, ice-wa-ter for blood. So

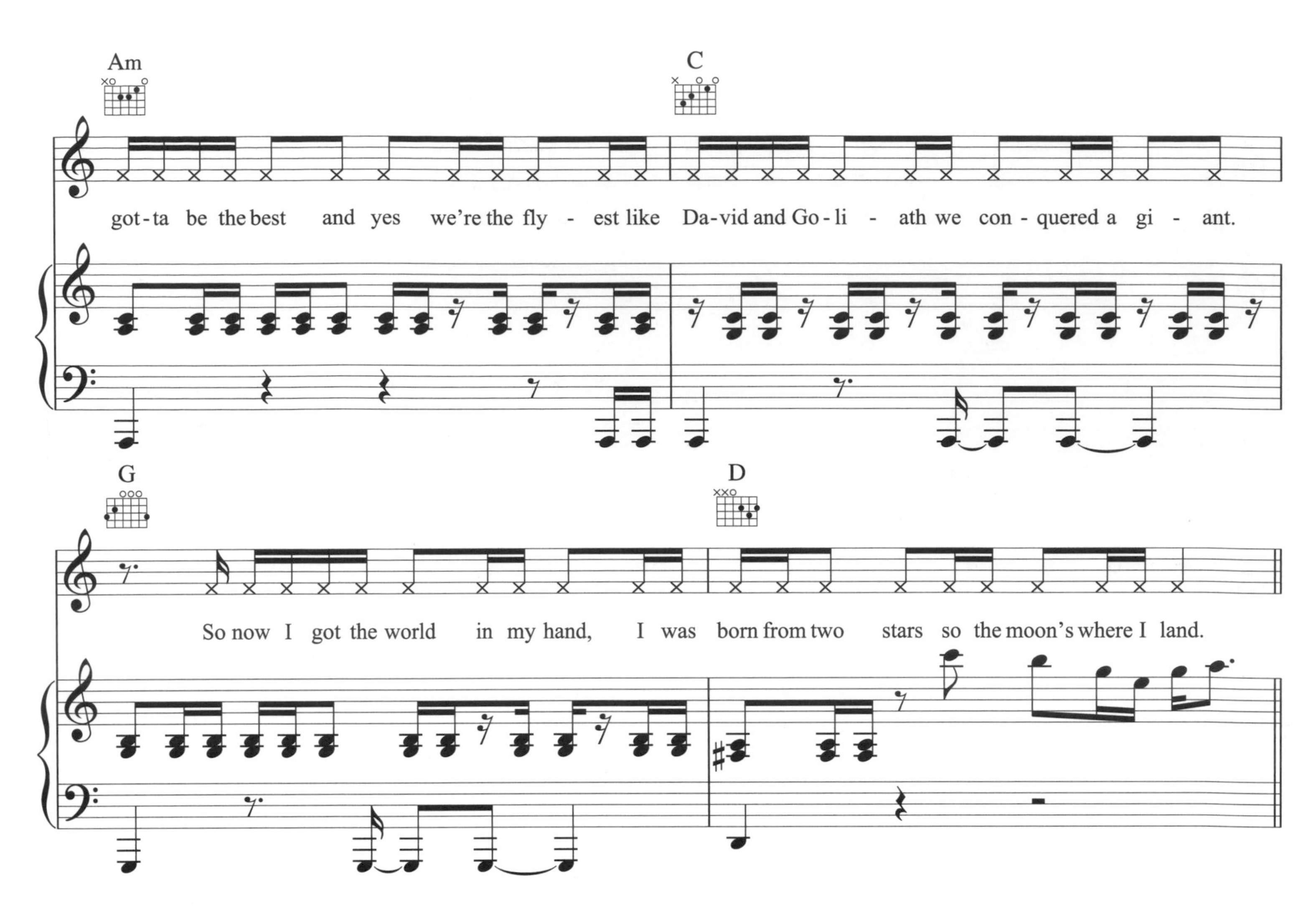
Am
C
got-ta be the best and yes we're the fly - est like Da-vid and Go-li - ath we con-quered a gi - ant.
G
D
So now I got the world in my hand, I was born from two stars so the moon's where I land.

F
C
G
F
C
I will nev-er say nev-er! (I will fight.) I will fight till for-ev-er!

G
F
C
G
(Make it right.) When-ev-er you knock me down, I will not stay on the ground.

Dm
Pick it up, pick it up, pick it up, pick it up, up, up and nev - er say nev - er.

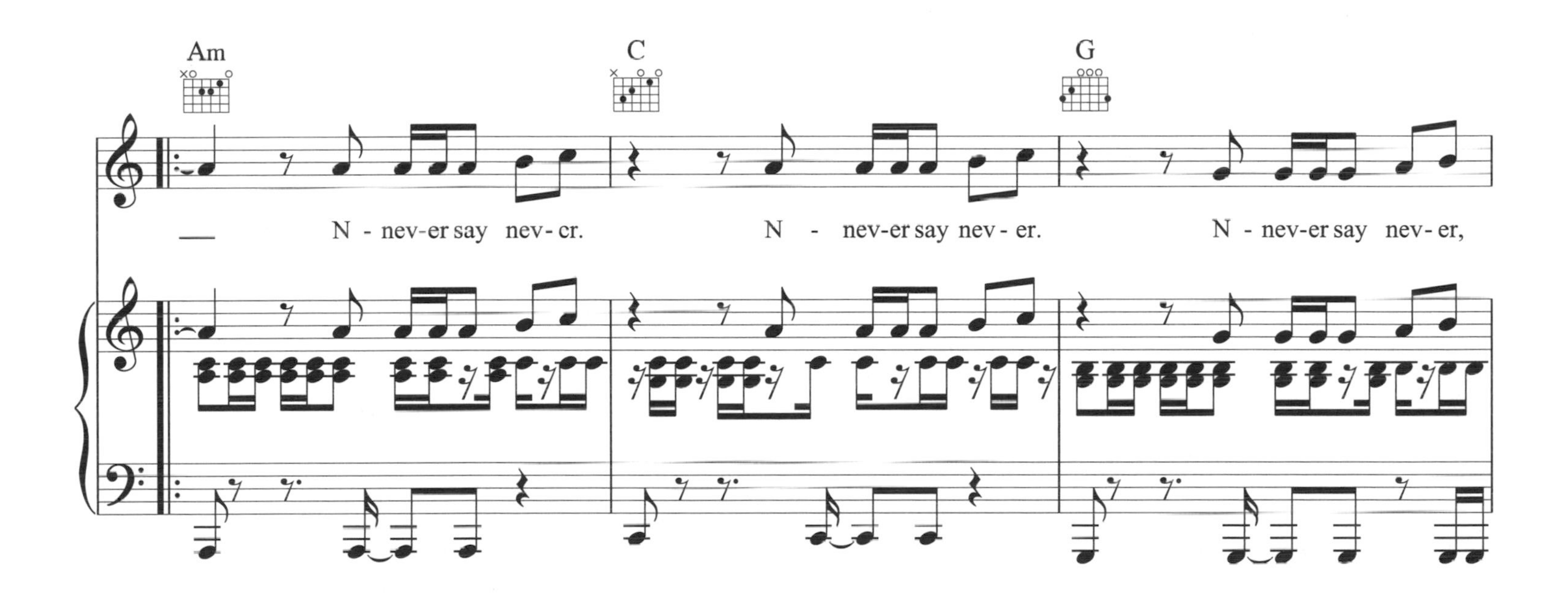
Am
C
G
N - nev-er say nev-cr.
N - nev-er say nev-er.
N - nev-er say nev-er,

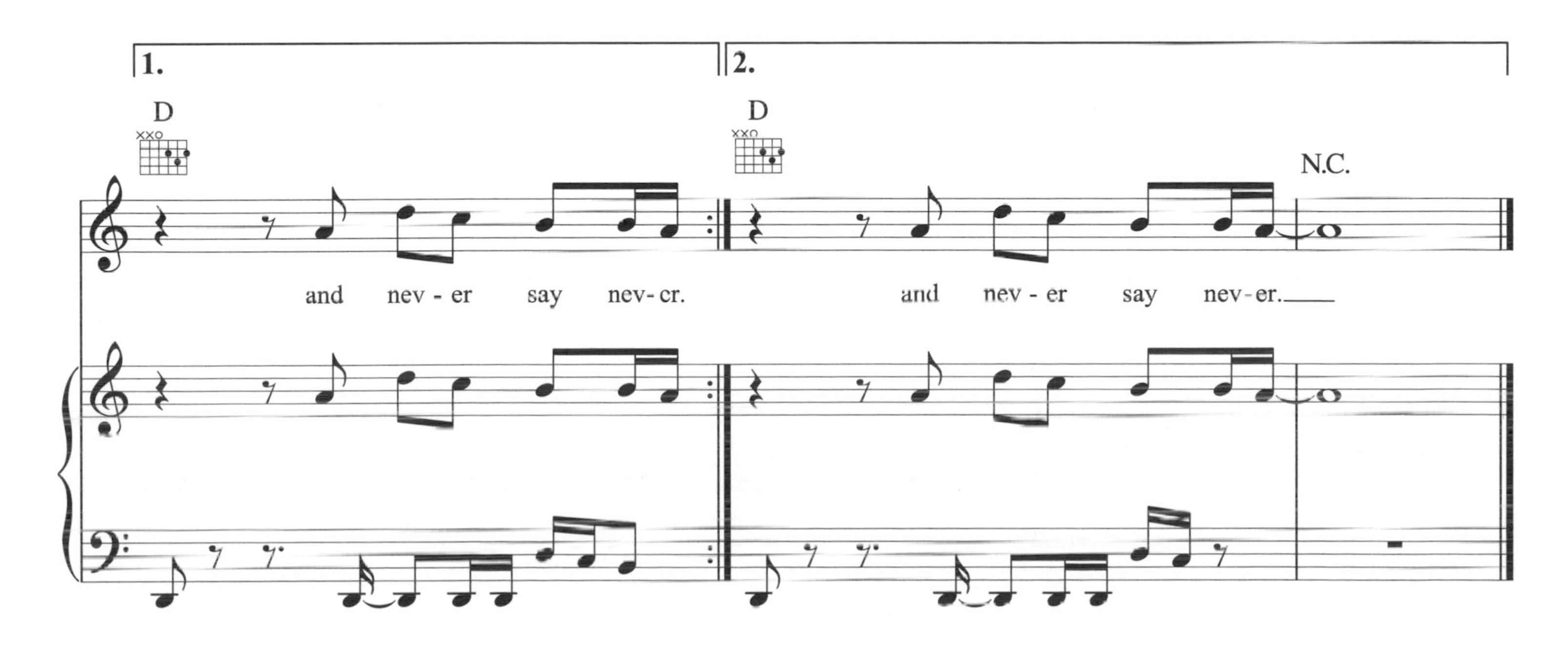
1.
2.
D
D
N.C.
and nev - er say nev-cr.
and nev - er say nev-er.

Pass Out

Words & Music by Mark Roberts, Patrick Okogwu
& Timothy McKenzie

Yeah. We bring the stars out. We bring the wom-en and the cars and the
cards out. Let's have a toast, a ce - le - bra - tion. Get a glass out and
we can do this un - til we pass out.
So let it rain.
Let it pour a - way. We won't
8vb
(8)

come down
un - til we hit the ground and
(8)
8vb
To Coda I
To Coda II N.C.
pass out.
3° Whoa
Yeah. I'm in charge now. I'm a
8vb
8vb
star and I brought my f***- in' cast out. I live a ver - y, ver - y, ver - y wild
(8)
8vb
life - style. Hei - di and Au - dri - na eat your heart out. I used to
8vb
8vb

lis - ten to you, don't wan - na bring arms out. I've got so man - y clothes I keep some in my
(8)
8vb
aunt's house. Dis - turb - ing Lon - don ba - by, we a - bout to branch out.
8vb
8vb
N.C.
Soon I'll be the king like Prince Charles' child. Yeah. Yeah. And there
(8)
8vb
ain't no - bod - y fresh - er se - mes - ter to se - mes - ter, rav - in' with the fresh - ers.
8vb
8vb

Twen-ty light bulbs a-round my ta-ble and my dress-er. C. L. C. Kom-pres-sor just in-
(8)
8vb
-case that don't im-press her. Say hel-lo to Dex-ter, say hel-lo to Un-cle Fes-ter. Got 'em
8vb
8vb
gaz-ing at my neck-lace and my cra-zy sun pro-tec - tors. G - shocks, I got a
(8)
8vb
D.S. al Coda I
cra-zy don col-lec - tion. Hat - ers, I can't f***-in' hear your re-cep - tion.
8vb
8vb

Coda I
N.C.
Yeah.
(Spoken:) This sh** was meant to last me 24 hours
razz.
O.K. I'm good.
Yeah.
1. They say hel -
N.C.
- lo, they say ho - la and they say bon - jour. I'm p***ed I nev - er got to fly on a
(2.) be a big - ger star than my mum thought 'cause ev - 'ry day I got a group - ie at my
8vb

Con - corde. I've been South - amp - ton but I've nev - er been to Scun - thorpe. I'm f***- in'
front door. Now I drive past the bus I used to run for.
8vb
8vb
cra - zy with the kicks, call me Jean Claude. 2. I'm 'bout to
Where's my f*** - in' clap, where's my en - core?
(8)
8vb
N.C.
I walk a - lone 'cause I was born a - lone. I chirps her just for fun, I'll
(8)
8vb
nev - er ev - er call her phone. I'll leave her in the club, I'll nev - er ev - er walk her home.
8vb
8vb

D. L. the f***-in' foun-da-tion, I'm the cor-ner-stone.
(8)
8vb
N.C.
I'm fair-ly fa-mous. I'm sor-ta known. And if your son does-n't
I bet your daugh-ter know. Check out my vi-su-al,
8vb
D.S. al Coda II
check out my au-di-o. Ex-tra-or-din-'ry, yo, hope you en-joy the show.
8vb
8vb

Coda II
Fm
B♭m
Fm
Whoa, oh, oh, oh, oh, oh,
2° only
3

B♭m
Fm
B♭m
oh, oh, oh. Whoa. Look at me I've been a cheek - y b*** - ard, man. And
3

Fm
B♭m
Fm
look at all the dra - ma we start - ed. Now I'm in here lay - in'
3

B♭m
Fm
B♭m
on my back sing - in' "D. J. won't you give me one more track?"
3
Perc.

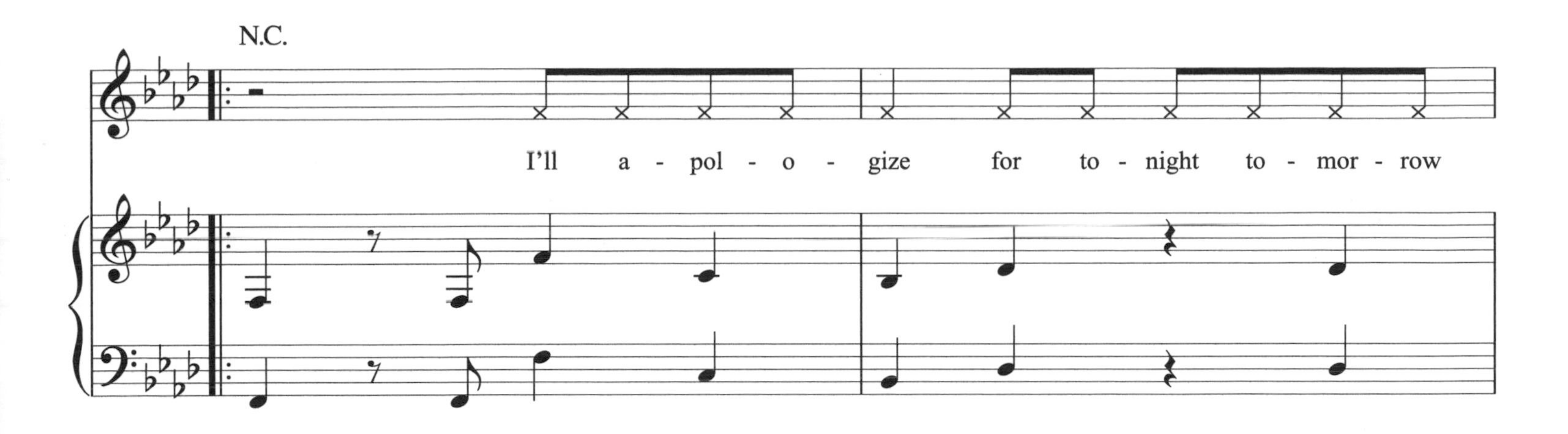
N.C.
I'll a - pol - o - gize for to - night to - mor - row

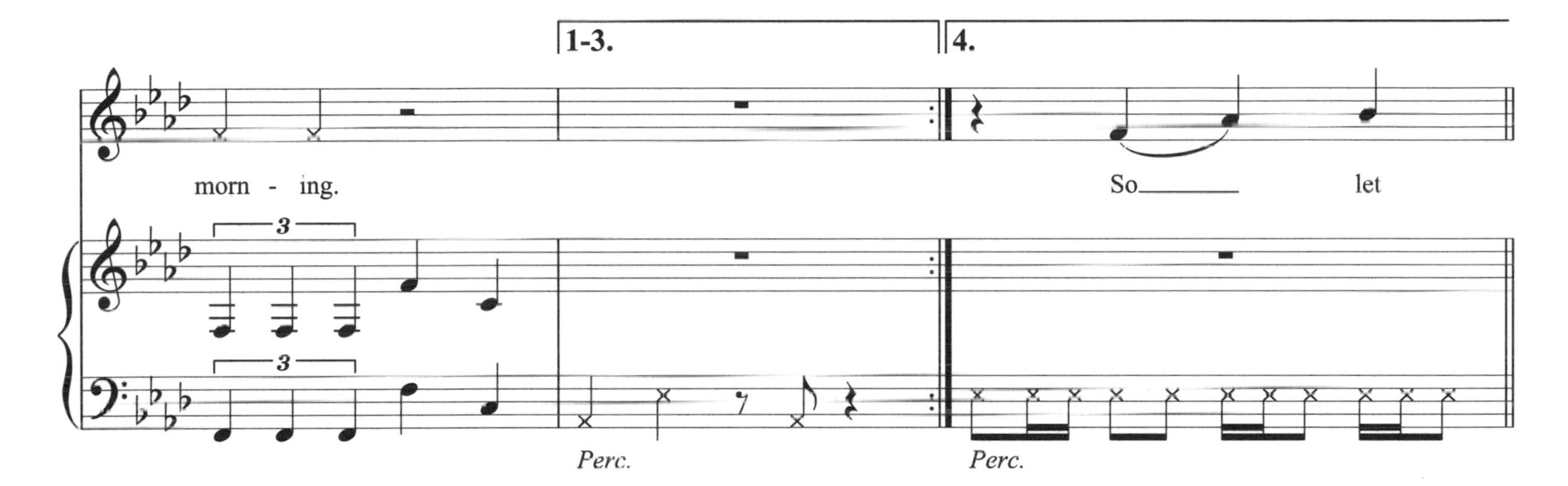
1-3.
4.
morn - ing.
So let
3
3
Perc.
Perc.

N.C.
it rain.
Let it pour a -
8vb
8vb

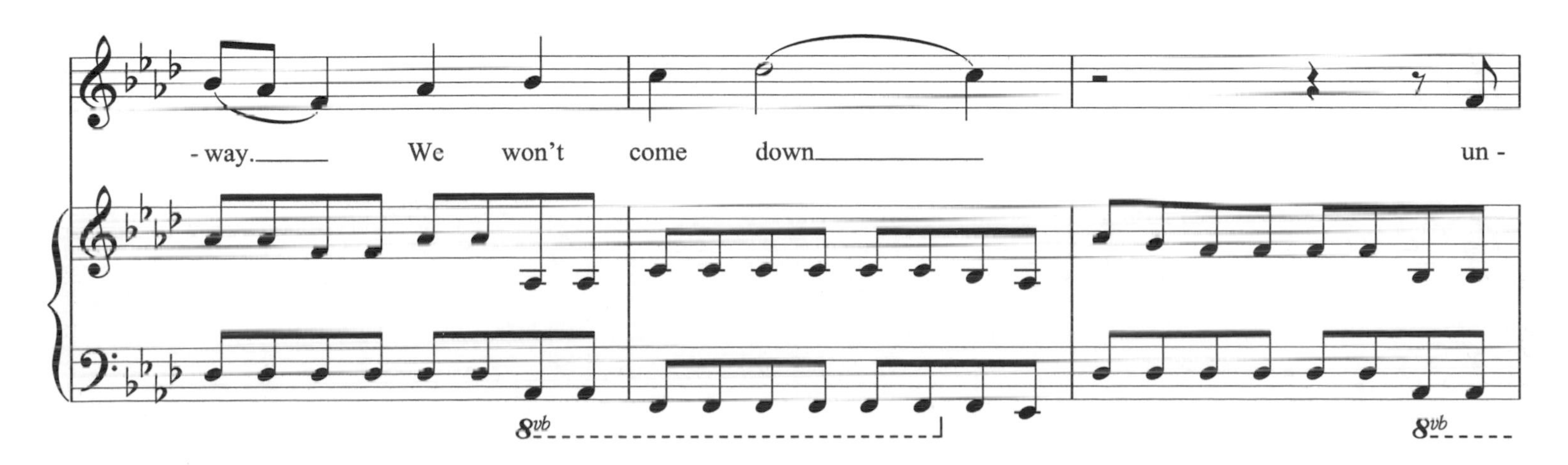
- way.
We won't come down
un -
8vb
8vb

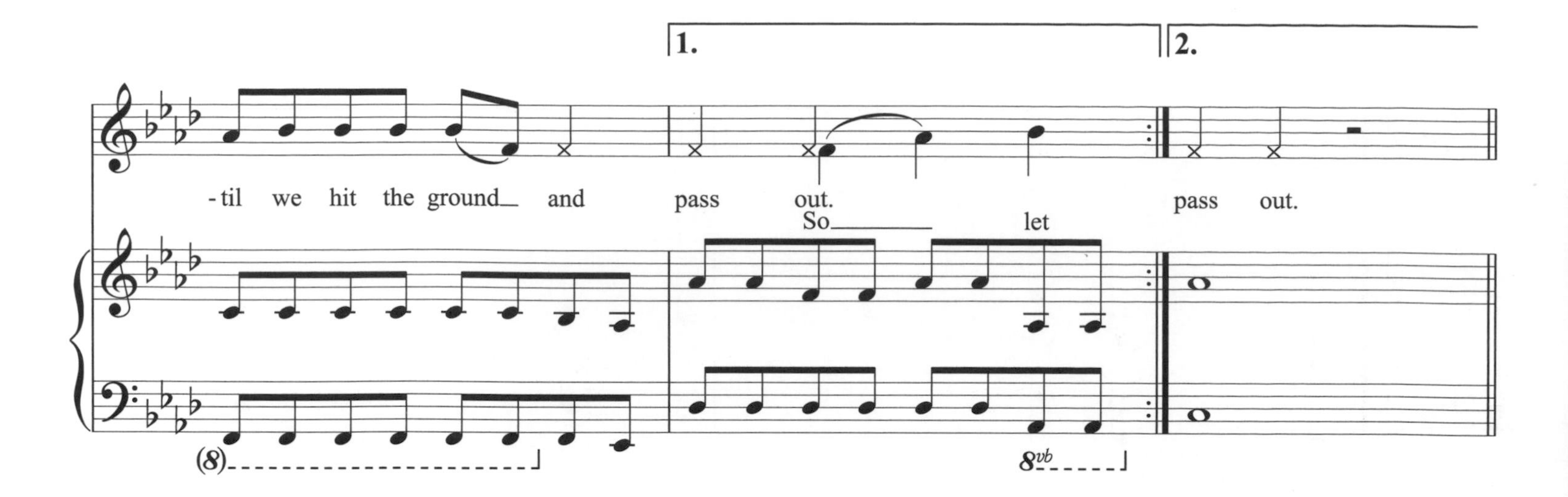
1.
2.
-til we hit the ground and pass out.
So let
pass out.
(8)
8vb

N.C.
8vb
8vb
8vb

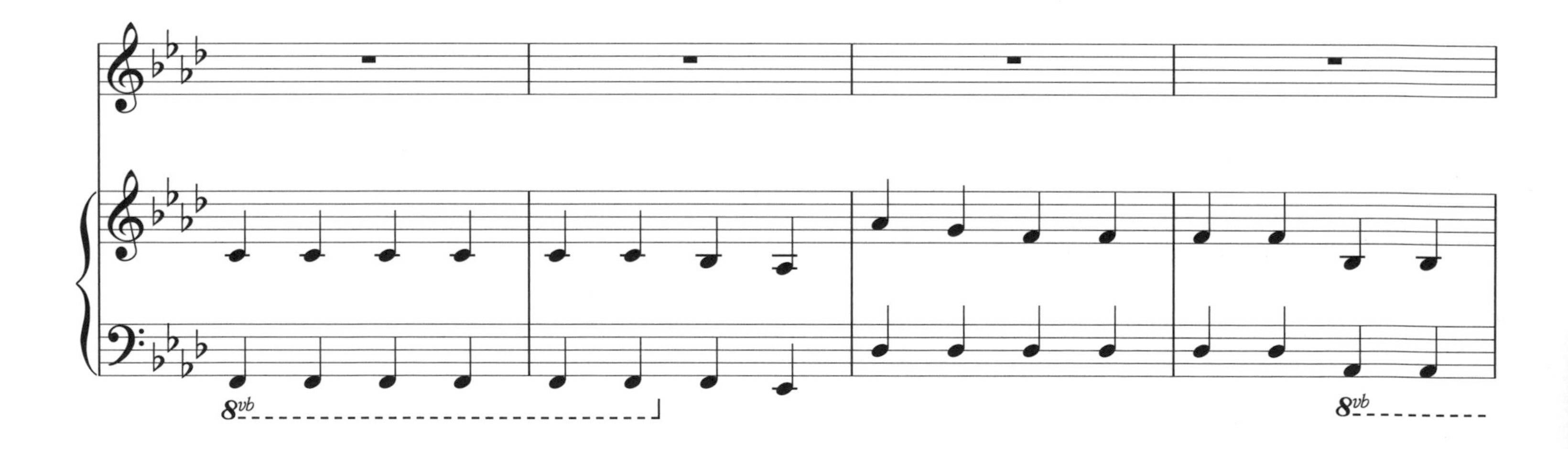
8vb
8vb

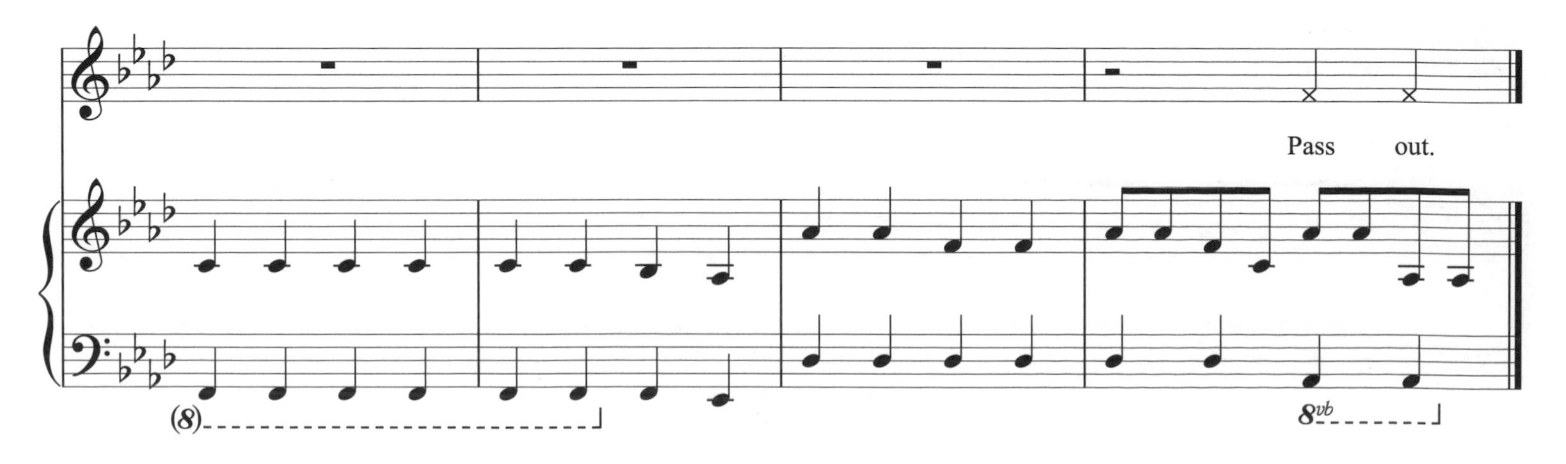
Pass out.
(8)
8vb

Price Tag

Words & Music by Lukasz Gottwald, Claude Kelly,
Bobby Ray Simmons & Jessica Cornish

Dm
B♭
night. When the sale comes first, and the truth comes se-cond, just stop for a min-ute and
-nite. And it wasn't low blows and video-o hoes, am I the only one get-ting
F
Am
smile. Why is ev-'ry-bod-y so se-ri-ous? Act-ing so damn mys-
tired? Why is ev-'ry-bod-y so ob-sessed? Mon-ey can't buy us
Dm
B♭
-ter-i-ous, got shades on your eyes and your heels so high that you can't e-ven have a good
hap-pi-ness. Can we all slow down and en-joy right now? Gua-ran-tee we'll be feel ing al-
F
Am
time.
-right.
Ev-'ry-bod-y look to their left, ev-'ry-bod-y look to their

Dm
N.C.
right. Can you feel that? Yeah, we're pay-ing with love to-night._ It's not a-bout the
F
Am
mon-ey, mon-ey, mon-ey._ We don't need your mon-ey, mon-ey, mon-ey._ We just wan na make the
Dm
B♭
world dance,_ for-get a-bout the price tag._ Ain't a-bout the
F
Am
(Uh.) cha-ching_ cha-ching. Ain't a-bout the (Yeah.) b-bling,_ b-bling. Wan-na make the

1.
2.
Dm
B♭
B♭
world dance, for-get a-bout the price tag. O. K. price tag. Yeah, yeah. Well, keep the
F
Am
price tag and take the cash back, just give me six strings and a half stack. And you can,
Dm
B♭
can keep the cars leave me the gar-age and all I, yes all I need are keys and gui-tars. And guess what,
F
Am
in thir-ty se-conds I'm leav-ing to Mars. Yeah, we leap-ing a-cross these un-de-feat-a-ble odds. It's like

Dm
this man, you can't put a price on the life.
B♭
We do this for the love so we fight and sac-ri-fice ev-'ry
F
night.
So we ain't gon' stum-ble and fall
N.C.
nev-er, nah. Wait-
Am
-ing to see this in the sign of de-feat,
N.C.
uh-uh. So
Dm
we gon' keep ev-'ry-one mov-ing their feet.
N.C.
So bring

B♭
back the beat and then ev - 'ry - one sing. It's not a - bout the
F
Am
mon- ey, mon- ey, mon ey. We don't need your mon- ey, mon- ey, mon ey. We just wan-na make the
Dm
B♭
world dance, for- get a - bout the price tag. Ain't a - bout the
F
Am
(Uh.) cha - ching cha- ching. Ain't a - bout the (Yeah.) b - bling, b- bling. Wan-na make the

1.
2.
Dm
B♭
F
Am
world dance, for-get a-bout the price tag. It's not a-bout the
price tag. Ah, ah,
ah, ah, yeah, yeah, oh.
For-get a-bout the price tag, yeah. Ah.

What The Hell

Words & Music by Avril Lavigne, Max Martin & Shellback

♩ = 155
A
D
F♯m
D

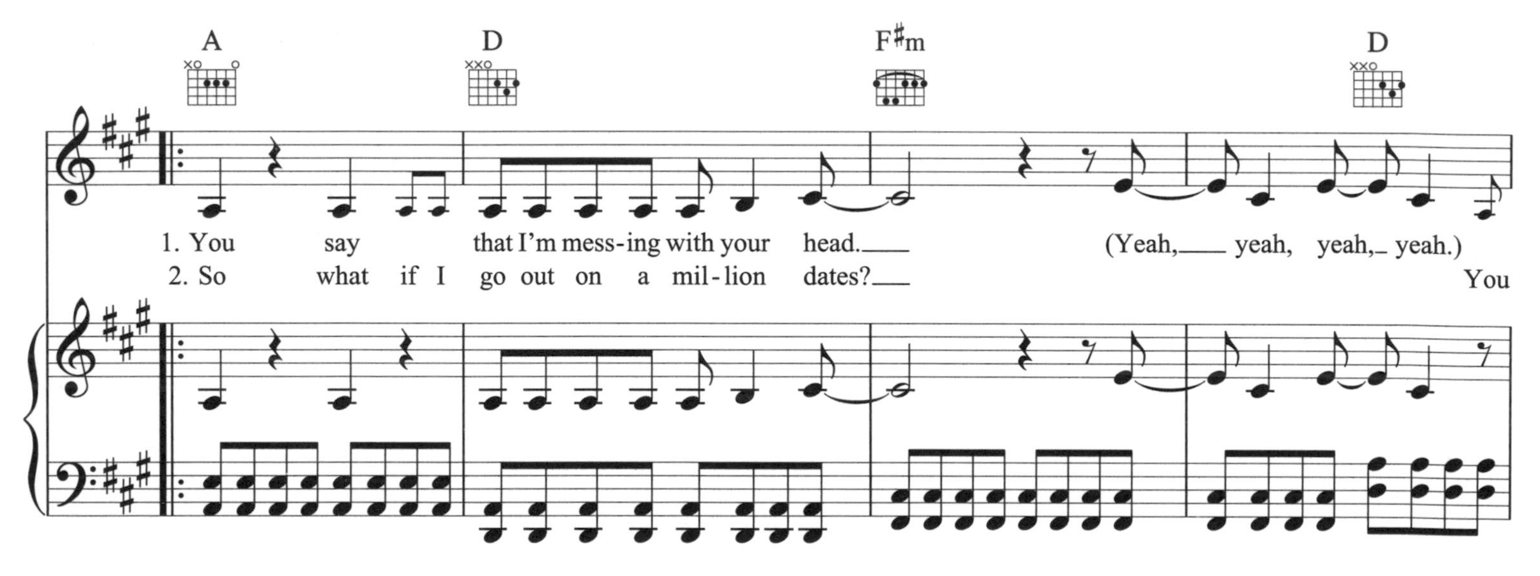
A
D
F♯m
D
1. You say that I'm mess-ing with your head.___ (Yeah,___ yeah, yeah,_ yeah.)
2. So what if I go out on a mil-lion dates?___ You

A
D
F♯m
D
All 'cause I was mak-ing out with your friend.___ (Yeah,___ yeah, yeah,_ yeah.)
nev - er call or lis-ten to me an - y - way.___ I

A
D
F#m
D
Love hurts wheth-er it's right or wrong. (Yeah, yeah, yeah, yeah.) I
ra - ther rage than sit a-round and wait all day. Don't
can't stop 'cause I'm hav - ing too much fun. (1° only) (Yeah, ycah yeah, yeah.) You're
get me wrong. I just need some time to play.
on your knees beg - ging please stay with me. But
hon - est - ly, I just need to be a lit - tle cra - zy

A
D
F♯m
D
All my life I've been good but now, oh, I'm think-ing what the hell.
All I want is to mess a-round and I don't real-ly care a-bout
if you love me, if you hate me, you can't save me, ba-by, ba - by.
All my life I've been good but now, whoa, what the hell.

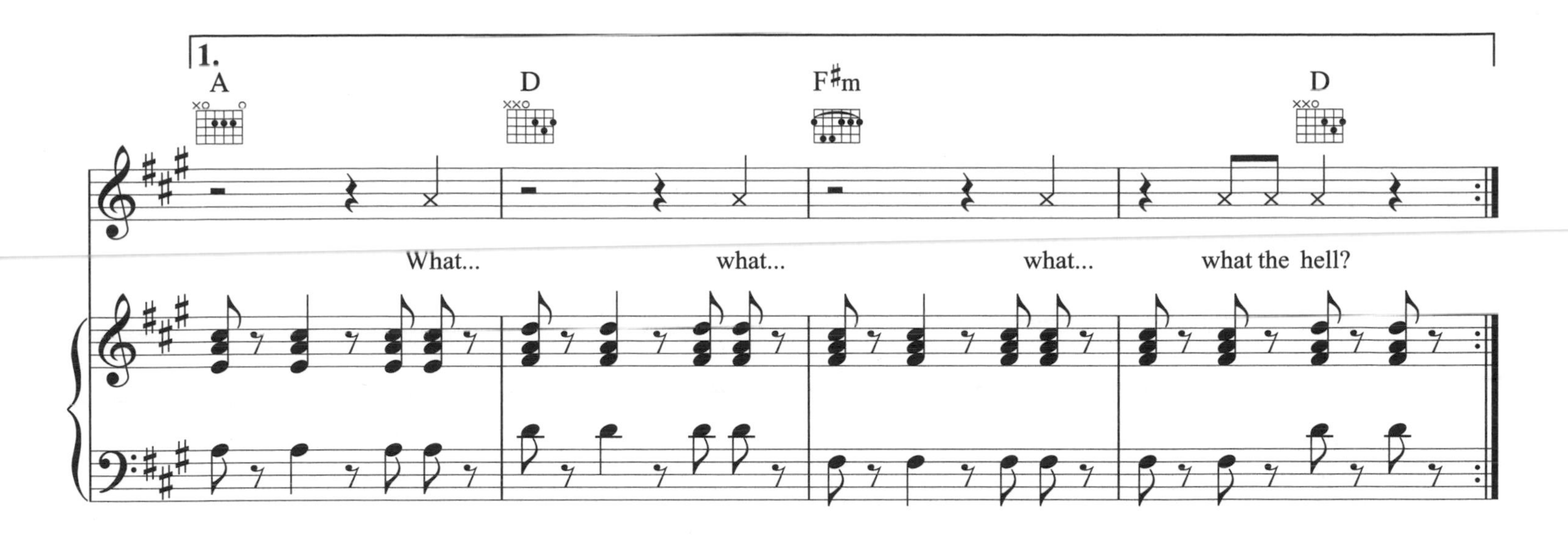
1.
A
D
F#m
D
What... what... what... what the hell?

2.
A
D
F#m
D

A
D
F#m
D
La, la, la, la, la, la, la, la... whoa... whoa...

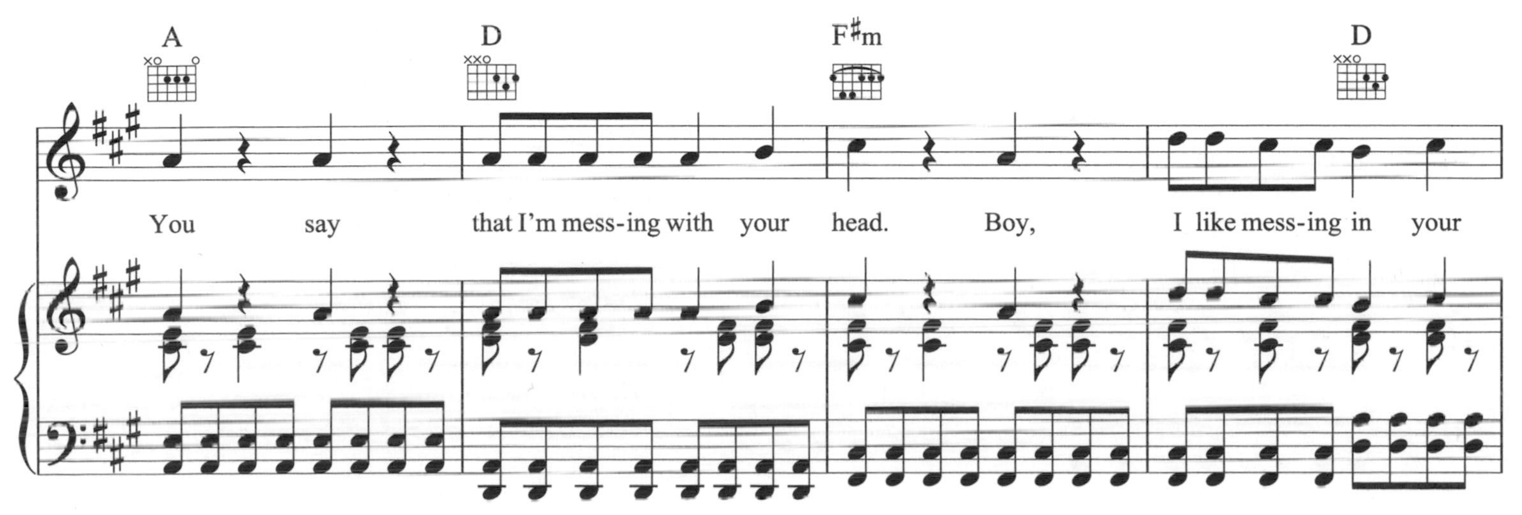
A
D
F#m
D
You say that I'm mess-ing with your head. Boy, I like mess-ing in your

A
D
F#m
D
bed. Yeah, I am mess-ing with your head when I'm mess-sing with you in
A
D
F#m
D
All my life I've been good but now, oh, I'm think-ing what the hell.
bed.
A
D
F#m
D
All I want is to mess a-round and I don't real-ly care a - bout...
A
D
F#m
D
All my life I've been good but now, oh, I'm think-ing what the hell.

A
D
F♯m
D
All I want is to mess a-round and I don't real-ly care a-bout
if you love me, if you hate me, you can't save me, ba-by, ba - by.
All my life I've been good but now, whoa, what the hell.
La, la, la, la, la, la, la, la, la, la, la, la, la, la, la, la, la.
N.C.

Someone Like You

Words & Music by Adele Adkins & Daniel Wilson

F#m
D
found a girl and you're mar-ried now.
yes - ter-day was the time of our lives. We were
A
C#m/G#
4fr
I heard that your dreams came true. Guess she
born and raised in a sum - mer haze. Bound

F#m
D
gave you things I did-n't give to you.
by the sur-prise of our glo - ry days. I

1° only
A
C#m/G#
4fr
Old friend, why are you so shy? Ain't like

F♯m
D
you to hold back, or hide from the light. I
Eadd9
F♯m7
D
hate to turn up out of the blue un-in-vit-ed but I couldn-n't stay a-way. I could-n't fight it. I had
Eadd9
F♯m7
D
Eadd9/D
hoped you'd see my face and that you'd be re-mind-ed that for me it is-n't o - ver.
1° only
D
2° only
D

A E F#m D
Nev-er mind I'll find some-one like you. I wish
8vb
A E F#m D
noth-ing but the best for you two. Don't for-
8vb
A E F#m D
-get me, I beg. I'll re-mem-ber you said some-times it
8vb
1, 3.
A E F#m D
lasts and loves but some-times it hurts in-stead. Some-times it
3
8vb

A
E
F♯m
D
To Coda ⊕
lasts and loves but some-times it hurts_ in - stead.
8vb
2.
F♯m
D
- stead.
8vb
E/B
F♯m/C♯
Noth-ing com-pares, no wor-ries or cares, re-grets and mis-takes, they are mem-o-ries made.
D5
5fr
E/B
A/C♯
2fr
Who would have known how bit-ter - sweet this would

rit.
a tempo
D
E/D
A
E/G♯
F♯m
D
taste?
Nev-er mind I'll find some-one like you. I wish
A
E/G♯
F♯m
D
A
E
noth-ing but the best for you. Don't for-get me, I beg. I'll re-
D.S. al Coda
F♯m
D
A
E/G♯
F♯m
D
-mem-ber you said some-times it lasts and loves but some-times it hurts in-stead.
Coda
D
G♯dim/D
Dmaj7
D5
A5
5fr

So Far Gone

Words & Music by James Blunt, Ryan B Tedder
& Stephen Paul Robson

A
D
2. We tried our best to find us, but there are no lights to guide us.
3. I've tried hard to re-mem-ber this pri-son cell used to be a shel-ter.

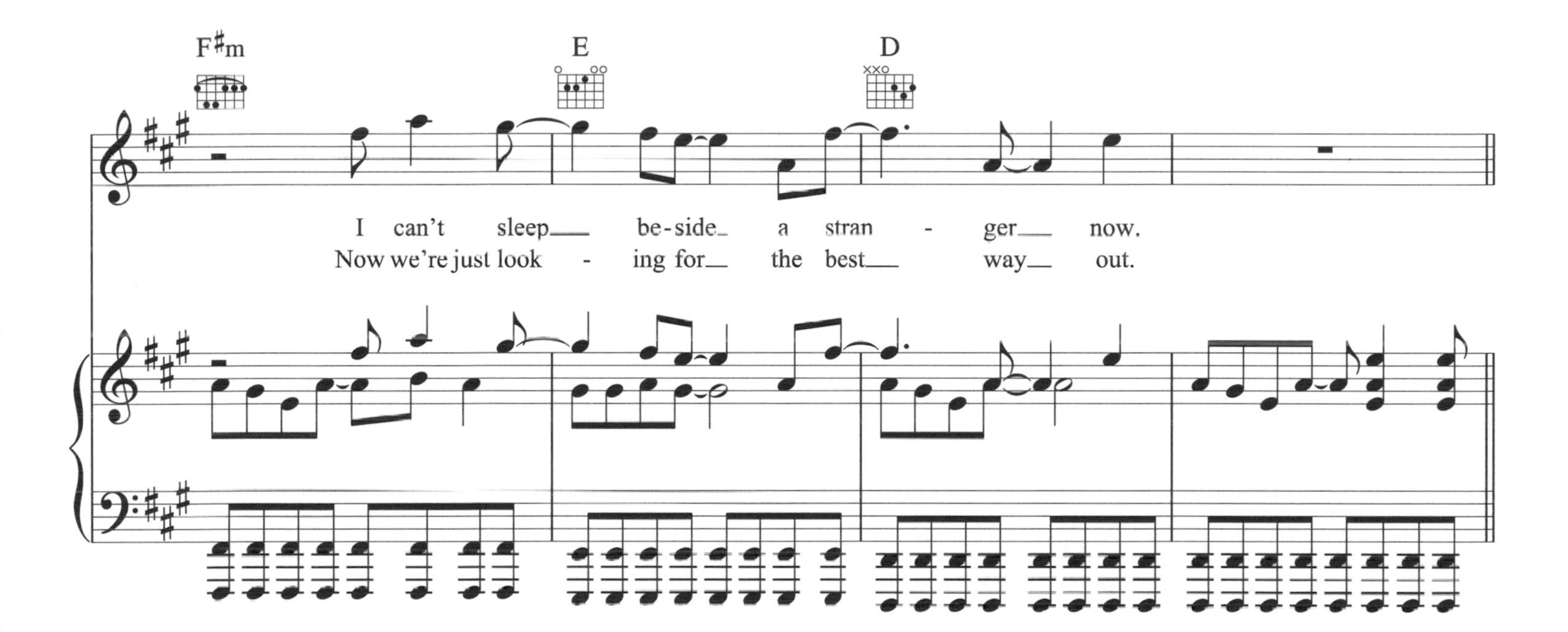
F♯m
E
D
I can't sleep be-side a stran-ger now.
Now we're just look-ing for the best way out.

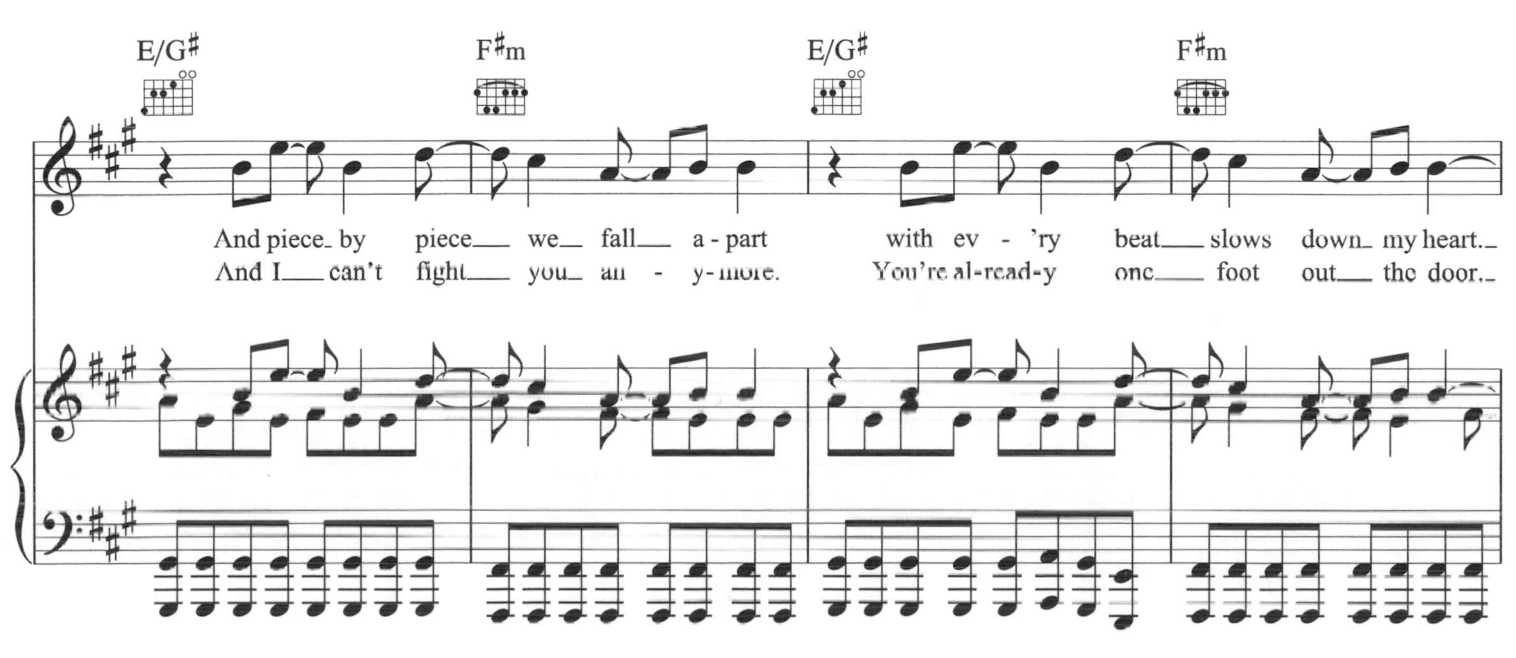
E/G♯
F♯m
E/G♯
F♯m
And piece by piece we fall a-part with ev-'ry beat slows down my heart.
And I can't fight you an-y-more. You're al-read-y one foot out the door.

E
D
A
E
(Ooh.)
So I'll just say
what you won't say
D
F♯m
E
D
and I'll take the blame
if it's for your sake.
No turn-ing back

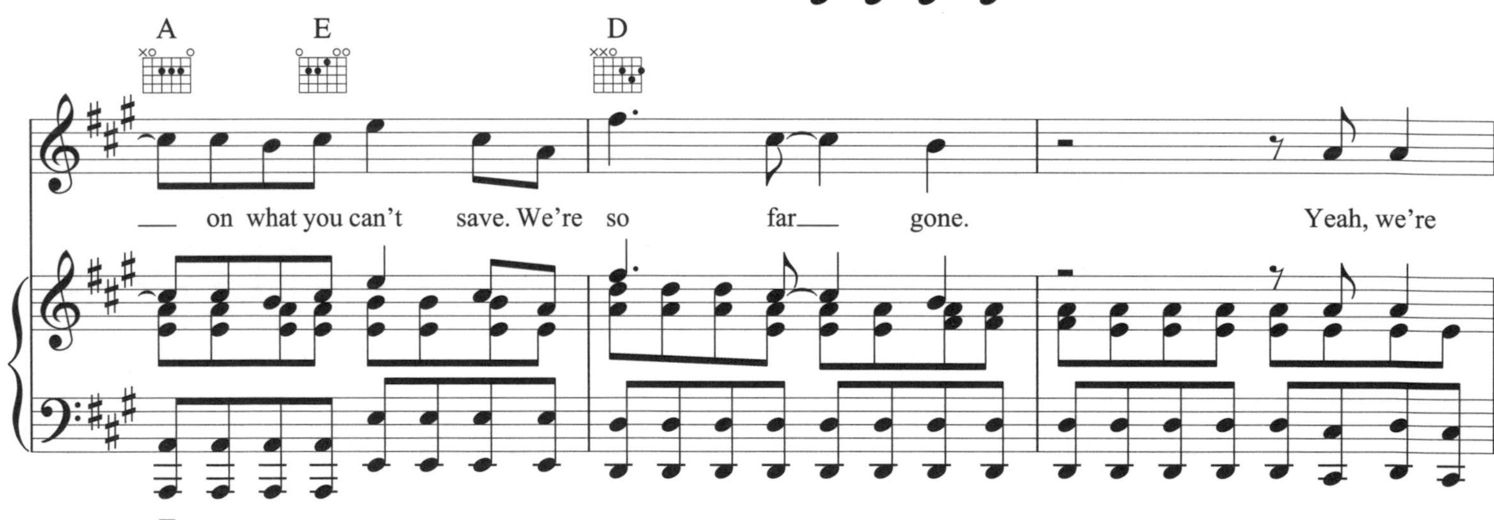
A
E
D
on what you can't save. We're so far gone.
Yeah, we're

E
1.
2.
so far gone.

Bm
A/C♯
E
And this is the face of let - ting go.

Bm
A/C♯
E
And these are the things we al - read-y know.

D
A
D
F♯m
E
So I'll just say what you won't say and I'll take the blame if it's for your sake.

D
A
E
D
E
No turn-ing back on what you can't save.
(Ooh.)

D
A
E
D
F♯m
E
So I'll just say what you won't say and I'll take the blame if it's for your sake.
D
A
E
D
No turn-ing back on what you can't save. We're so far gone. Yeah, we're

Bm
E
so far gone. Yeah, we're so far gone.

D
F♯m
E
So I'll just say what you won't say.

1 2 3 4 5 6 7 8 9